Footsteps
to
Freedom

Footsteps

to

Freedom

28380

BY

LEVI O. KEIDEL, JR.

MOODY PRESS • CHICAGO

This book is dedicated to Congolese heroes of the faith whose personal experiences are related herein, and whose lives are a tremendous challenge to my own spiritual commitment.

Preface

Several books have already been written by missionaries who passed through Congo's trying tempests of political upheaval.

This book is written from the viewpoint of Congolese who were caught in the vortex of these storms and bore their full fury. Their suffering has been infinitely greater than that of the white missionaries. Their heroism, unheralded, began more than a generation ago.

In this book a Congolese Christian, in his own simple way, tells the story of his life and of his people. Many of the events are documented incidents from the life of a Congolese pastor who is a personal friend of mine. Some events have been related to me by other Congolese Christians with whom I have labored since 1951. Others, such as the widespread anti-government rebellion of 1964, I experienced with them.

All events have been placed in story form so that the narrative of the Congolese could be woven smoothly around a single person, Mulumba.

Levi O. Keidel, Jr.

1

This is the voice of Mulumba. I do not speak alone. As the thunder of a great river is the voice of many streams, so my voice is the words of many people. They tell you of Congo.

My Congo.

I do not tell you legends. I tell you affairs that have happened—affairs that our fathers told us when we were children and sat with them at the fire—affairs that we could not believe—affairs that now we have seen—affairs that have made minds wise as elders' while bodies are yet young.

My story is like footprints. Some footprints are of long ago—footprints which have disappeared from eyes many days—footprints remembered well only by the ears of the earth. Other footprints will lead through jungles—jungles with darkness so black our eyes cannot see. And others will lead us through rushing waters—waters so strong they make us fall—waters red with blood of men. They will lead us where the sun shines brightly, where our hearts sing like birds. With me you will weep, you will sing, you will pray.

My story begins with the moon—the great round moon of my childhood. It whitened the earth between our huts. It frightened the spirits back into the jungle. I did not yet hunt with the hunters. I did not yet hoe in the fields. I was a child among children and we sang and danced in the great moon's light.

I remember how we felt sadness when the great moon was finished and darkness returned. Spirits became bold again and came back out of the forest. We heard them talking when wind shook the leaves high up in the trees above our heads. Then we could not laugh and play. We would sit close to the fire. We felt safer within its light.

Then, by the fire, our fathers would speak words of wisdom. They told us fables—how the goat earned its name, why the coyote and the dog broke their covenant of friendship forever, how the turtle surpassed the crocodile in wisdom.

They warned us of the spirits who did cruel things in the darkness. They told us how to appease the anger of the spirits; thus the spirits would do us no harm, and would be at peace with us.

Our fathers told us of Mvidi Mukulu, the great elder Spirit. He was not like other spirits. He was brighter than the sun. He brought us everything good.

Mvidi Mukulu created all things. He created people. He wanted to talk with them. To do this, He sent them His Child.

When the Child grew up, He had power to do magic which passed up that of the witch doctors. He taught the people. His teaching showed the people their sins. It made them feel guilty, like dogs caught stealing meat. They could not understand His magic. They were afraid of Him. They did not like Him. They said to each other, "We must kill Him. How can we catch Him?"

One day after He had finished teaching He was tired and hungry. It was time to eat. He saw inside a hut good food, steaming food. They asked Him to eat it. He went into the hut. They tied the door shut and burned the hut. They rejoiced. "Now He is gone forever," they said.

When the fire was finished, they could not find His body.

8

They did not know where He had gone. After some days news came from a village far away. The Son of Mvidi Mukulu was teaching again. More people than before were listening to Him. The people who burned the hut were sad, like hunters when an animal escapes their trap. They had failed to kill Him. He had surpassed them in power. He was stronger than death.

When I heard about the Son of Mvidi Mukulu, He made me think of the moon. He seemed close like the moon. He could not be destroyed, but came back again, like the moon. Where was He teaching now? I wanted to find Him. Like the moon whitened the earth, could He whiten my heart? Could He frighten the spirits forever back into the darkness? Could He, like the moon, make me, Mulumba, happy and sing?

Many times my father told the story of where we had come from. My brother and sister sat with me. We watched our father closely. We listened well. He showed us these footprints of long ago.

The land of our forefathers is far away. It is the distance of a foot journey of two tens of days. It is where the sun gets up in the morning. There hills rise and fall like smooth waves on the lake when the wind blows softly. When one stands on top of a hill, he can see only the green grass of other hills. Between the hills, where one cannot see, there are forests and streams and bubbling springs. Our forefathers were happy in that land, and the moons passed, no one counting them.

During the moons when rain does not fall, the air becomes dry as the breath of an antelope who has lost its path to water and stands panting in a strange wilderness. The sky becomes gray with fog and hides the sun for many days. The sky, as a great cloth carrying a growing burden of dust, slowly comes down to meet us. Earth begins

9

to cry for water. Tree leaves become heavy with red dust; they hold their faces upward, waiting to be washed. The grass, which encloses villages like a wall high as the houses, becomes dry and brittle, like trees of straw.

Then our forefathers would burn the grass. With arrows and spears, they killed animals fleeing from the fire. They skinned the animals and covered their bodies with the soft hides. They went to tribes near them and traded meat for tools of iron. They ate meat until they were filled. They rejoiced.

They got their food from fields which they made during the dry moons. Near a stream, with knives and axes, they cut down the forest. They gathered the dried branches and vines and burned them. They cleaned the ground well. Then with hoes, they planted their grain and returned to their villages to wait for the moons of rain to begin.

Our forefathers knew that the spirits of their ancestors continued to live among them. They received good things because these spirits were pleased; they received misfortune because these spirits were grieved. Thus they prayed to Mvidi Mukulu and worshiped these spirits so their lives would be blessed with good affairs.

The spirits were worshiped by well-arranged customs. They were worshiped at the miabi[1] tree. A piece of this special tree was brought from the forest and erected like a post in the corner of a family compound. On it was carved the face of a person. Here the family talked with its ancestral spirits.

The father would sit with his wife and children before the miabi tree. He would slay a white chicken and place its blood on the miabi post. Then he would lift the chicken toward heaven and pray:

---

[1] Miabi, pronounced myăbee.

Great One who shows love,
Who is too bright for the sun to look at,
Make us pure, that You can look at us.
Give us strength.
Let sorcerers, let enemy spirits,
Let evil things, let men of hatred
Flow with the water downstream
And disappear forever.

The mother would cook the chicken and a mush loaf of bidia.[2] She would take this food to the miabi tree. The father would give the first portion of the food to the spirits, placing it upon the post. Then he would eat his portion. Then he would give the mother her portion. Then he would give the children theirs. When they had finished eating, and the father had confessed their sins to the spirits, they would rise together and go to their house quietly, not looking back lest the spirits follow them.

This was life when my father first appeared on earth. He played with his three brothers and sister and other children. In the moons of no rain, when the grass was burning, they ran over the hills, following the fires. Their feet became hot from the stubble; their legs were blackened with soot.

When the rains returned, they played hunters-and-animals on the edge of the jungle. They sat with their child-bows and arrows in the fields and shot at monkeys who came from the forest to eat the tender grain plants. They sneaked from home to go see the caves in the stone hills along the great river Lomayi. With much fear, they would peer into the darkness of the entryways, fleeing when evil spirits inside chased bats out into the sunlight.

For many seasons of rain, this was the picture of the childhood life of Father. It was a peaceful life, a happy life,

---

[2] Bidia, pronounced beedya.

a life that moved on and on like a smooth stone rolling slowly down a long hill.

Then one day strange men came with killing-things in their hands. These things were not bows which shot arrows. They were sticks that spoke like lightning and threw fire. When the fire sticks came, happiness ended.

At first my father's people just heard words. Then strange black tribesmen with fire sticks came and made war on a nearby village. The fire sticks spoke. When they spoke, they ate meat off the legs of some, they punched holes in the bellies of others. Some village people fled. Other people were caught and tied with vines and led off like captured animals. When those who had escaped returned to their village, they found bodies of their clansmen chewed as if by angry lions. Many of their clansmen with strong bodies had disappeared. Many of their huts were burned; other huts were left empty, like broken eggshells. Villages were left with few people. Mourning never ceased.

When these words first reached my father's village, people's hearts split with fear. Where had these tribesmen come from? Where had they found the fire sticks? What did they do with our people? Will they come to catch us? If they do, how shall we escape? Where shall we hide, lest their fire sticks chew us up and make us their slaves forever?

Wars had come before. A few people would be wounded and a few killed. Then the chiefs would make a covenant of peace. But this was another kind of war. The villages' oldest wise men could remember nothing like it.

After some days, other words arrived—words that made knees tremble with weakness and hearts become like water.

Strange tribesmen had not ceased to burn villages. As people butcher animals, so these men butchered people, using their fire sticks. Their hunger for people could not be satisfied. They caught the young and strong, and those who

12

were caught disappeared from earth forever. We could not fight against warriors such as these. We could not stop them by a covenant of peace.

Hard affairs caught our people rapidly. One night, after the tall grass had been burned, nearby there was the sound of many bolts of lightning; then there were screams of people, injured people, fleeing people. The people-stealers were making war on the village of our clansmen just over the hill. Our village would be next. This was the end of all good things. As a clay pot thrown to the ground, the happy life was suddenly broken into pieces that could never be mended.

In my father's village, all but those weak with sickness or age fled. But there was no tall grass to hide them. "Let us run to the great river Lomayi," they cried. "Let us hide in its caves."

They ran toward the river. They reached the cave entryway. They stopped. With hearts pounding, they stared into the darkness. Fear of the strange foreigners with fire sticks was greater than their fear of evil spirits in the darkness. They entered the cave. The children, filled with fear, sat on the stone floor to rest. Parents cut tree branches and covered the entryway. They piled big stones behind the branches until the entryway was closed and all was dark; then they sat trembling, like animals in a strange den.

They waited for what seemed like many days; they could not count the days in the darkness. They could not lay their babies on blankets of elephant leaves for such things do not grow in caves. They could not put their babies down; the bats would bite them.

They drank water that dripped from the ceiling but ate nothing. Because of fear, because of hunger, because of crying little ones, because of coldness that made their limbs

13

stiff as sticks, they slept little. Men talked of sneaking out to get something for the children to eat.

Suddenly they heard the noises they had feared. Were those voices of people? Yes, angry voices talking in a strange tongue. Those who spoke were standing at the entryway.

Suddenly a stone moved. Light cut the darkness and hurt eyes. The black face of a strange man appeared. He saw the people sitting, fearing. He cried out in surprise. He called others.

They opened the entryway. They shouted. An iron stick spoke and threw fire into the air. They caught our people and tied their hands behind their backs. They tied my father, his brothers and sister to their parents. They tied people together, one after another, with a long vine. Then they made the people-vine begin to move. Slowly, as sheep move toward the place of butchering, the people-line began moving along the path toward where the sun sets.

For my people, this day was a day of sorrow, bitter sorrow, sorrow unto death. For my tribe, it was a day of shame, great shame such as they had never known. My father was but a child, yet he knew that after today, he would never see his homeland again. He knew they were going to where many of their tribemates had already disappeared.

They were going to a strange land—a land which was foreign to our family's ancestral spirits—a land whose spirits spoke other tongues, and would not hear their vows of worship at the miabi tree. They were going to a land which had never yet felt the weight of their feet, or the cutting of their hoes. Yes, this was the end of all good things. And yet, though Father did not know it, even greater shame than this would come.

The tears of my people ran down like rivers of water. As a

14

great loud wail, their song of mourning was lifted to the sky.

O Earth beneath us,
You who alone have ears forever open,
You remember our forefathers' footsteps,
The thump thump of feet with much burden,
Like pestle pounding in mortar,
When they were driven off captive
And caused to be beasts of burden.

They have not gone off forever.
As the sun must wake up tomorrow,
We will hear their footsteps again.
You will bring us the sound of their walking
Like marching men going into battle,
Like hunters light-footed in forest,
Like men who harvest the gardens,
Like feet that dance in the moonlight—
The footsteps of men who are free.

2

As animals trapped in the burning grass, our people were trapped in the burning sun. The young and strong were taken first; they wanted to walk rapidly. Parents with children walked more slowly. The old followed behind. Because the vine tied them all, they all walked the same speed.

Little by little, the hours passed. Bodies of people became gray with dust. Sweat ran down their faces and backs as tiny rivers, cutting paths through the dust. Thirsty flies drank from the rivers. Tied hands could not chase them away.

When the sun lowered behind the hills, they stopped at a stream. Hands were untied, people washed their bodies, then hands were tied again for the night. But the vine which tied people together was not cut. Bowels and bladders were eased in the darkness. Animals were fortunate—each finds its own place. But it was not thus with our people; they were shamed together.

At night, in the place of heat came cold. In the place of flies came mosquitoes. The air was full of the warm smell of excretion which could not be covered.

Thus the first day passed, the first night passed, many days and nights passed. These foreign tribesmen, their black masters, holding in their hands whips of hippopotamus hide, drove them forward. Hunger wasted their strength. The fear of death made them forget honor and pride.

My father was made to walk in front of his parents, for they did not want their children to see older people who stumbled and fell. If one who stumbled could not rise, the vine was cut and tied again, and a weak body remained behind as the joy feast of a hyena or leopard.

When they arrived at the village of their black masters, the line had shortened. Aged tribemates following behind my father and his parents were few. My people were no longer strong, proud people. They were like two-legged beasts who obeyed because they wanted to remain alive. All were made to sit on the ground in a circle outside a hut. Then from the hut came something that made their hearts split with fear.

It had two legs and two arms like a person, but it was colorless, as the flesh of fish. It was straight and tall, like a stalk of grain. Its nose was long and pointed and its lips were thin. Its chest and arms and legs were covered with cloth. Its head was covered with a white hat which looked like a tiny round hut with a wide veranda. Its feet had no toes, like a leper's. It was a ghost in the body of a person.

It was a white man.

The vine was cut. Young men and women were gathered into one group. The white man made them stand. He looked at the body of each of them carefully; then he counted them—fourteen. Two helpers brought a heavy box from the white man's hut. From it he took fire sticks and counted them on the ground—fourteen. He gave them to our masters. This answered many questions, and the answers made our people fear exceedingly.

Though fear was great, hunger was greater. Food was prepared. My people's hands were untied. They ate well. Their hands were not retied after the meal. When darkness came, sleep caught them for the first time in many nights.

When the sun rose, the white man, with four strong helpers, retied our young men and women. They took them down a jungle path and disappeared. Our people have a custom: when death takes a loved one away forever, everyone mourns for many days. This time many of our loved ones were taken away forever, but because bodies were weak and hearts were afraid, no one mourned.

By the time several months had passed, Father's people learned that the white man had been friends with their black masters for many years. He had taught them that they exceeded all other tribes in wisdom and if they continued to work with him, he would help them become masters of all the tribes of the land. Someday they would be chiefs of a great kingdom of black men. Their hearts, as the jaws of a crocodile, held onto his words tightly.

The white man had a kingdom also. It was far across the great water. Some said he was white because of the much water through which he had passed to reach us. Because of the great distance to his kingdom, he wanted only strong young people. Married people were kept as slaves of the black tribesmen. Father's parents were made the slaves of a village elder. Elders helped the village chief rule his people.

Father, though yet a child, feared growing up. He feared the day the white man would return and find his body strong and would take him down the jungle path to disappear forever.

Years passed. Visits of the white man became less and less. The black sand-medicine which made the fire sticks speak was used up. Thus the fire sticks spoke no more. They sat uselessly inside huts and became covered with rust, dust, and spider webs. There remained only one thing to fear—the hippopotamus hide whip.

The whip of my grandparents' master hung on a post in his compound. It was seldom used. Grandfather had a big body. He had much strength. His face did not show the sadness of his heart. He and grandmother worked well. They tilled their master's gardens and trapped his meat.

They gathered his firewood and drew his water. They swept his compound. They repaired the houses of his many wives. Their children helped them and developed strong bodies.

But no matter how hard they worked, their wages were the same—something to eat and something to cover their bodies.

There was a burden greater than their work. It was the burden that tortured their hearts. They were not people. They were not even as animals which roamed the forest with freedom. They were as captured animals, animals that always worked for another. It would be this way tomorrow, the next day, forever.

Maybe the white man would return, maybe he would not. No one knew. My father reached adulthood. Quickly his parents arranged a marriage for him. He had known the girl since childhood. The bride-price of two gourds of palm wine was paid to her parents and thus the marriage covenant was sealed.

My father and his bride found joy—joy they had not known since they played as children in their homeland. But this was a new kind of joy—joy in each other's love. Love could not be shown in the daylight. It could only be shared in the darkness, inside their hut. This joy could not be stolen from them. They drank it as people with much thirst. Its greatness made their burden lighter.

When a sufficient number of days passed, a girl child was born. They named her Disanka, which means joy. She would give them the joy they would need in the years ahead of them. After more days a second girl child came. They named her Ditekemena, which means hope. This name would always remind them of their hope that someday, they or their seed would be released from their bonds of slavery and become people again.

Because of the little children, the joy of my father and

19

mother was complete and abundant. Now they held in their arms something they could call their own. This, their seed, would remain on the earth after them. Truly, they were still slaves, but they had begun to fulfill the purpose of people upon earth. Their yoke of shame lightened. They were still young. They felt strong and brave.

The vine starts as a small thing, yet it grows and winds itself around and around the tree trunk until it encloses it tightly. It grasps the tree trunk forever. Thus grew Disanka and Ditekemena. Disanka, holding Mother's finger tightly in her hand, went with her to the forest and to the spring. When they returned, Mother carried a great load on her head. Disanka followed closely, carrying on her head a piece of firewood or a tiny gourd filled with water. Ditekemena spent many days with Father in the fields. Disanka and Ditekemena grew slowly until, like the vine, they enclosed the hearts of their parents forever.

One day Father and Ditekemena were in the field. The time was afternoon, when the sun begins entering behind the trees. Suddenly lightning spoke three times and Father's heart split with fear. How could lightning speak when the sun was shining? There was no rain in the sky. But this sound did not come from above, it came from the direction of the village. Lightning speaking in the village? No. It could not be. Fire sticks. That's what it was. Fire sticks! It had been so long he had almost forgotten their sound.

What would he do? He would pick up Ditekemena and run far into the forest. They would hide in the darkest place, where no one could ever find them. They would live on roots and berries and animals they trapped. Perhaps they could flee to their homeland and freedom.

But what of Disanka and her mother? When he failed to return, his master would beat them. Or the new visitor with the fire stick might carry them off forever. Father fought in his heart. He could not flee with Ditekemena and leave Disanka and her mother to suffering he did not know. He must return with Ditekemena to the village. He might be leading her to death, but it is better for hearts woven as one to die together than for them to be severed and suffer from wounds that would not heal forever.

When it was dusk, Father and Ditekemena sneaked as animals evading a hunter around the edge of the village to their hut. Disanka and her mother were safe. "The visitors are at the chief's house," Mother said. "A white man and eight big black men. All have fire sticks."

"What do they want?" Father asked.

"They want food," Mother answered.

Father knew they had also come for other things. Had the white man returned to fulfill his promise to make this tribe the masters of all tribes of the land? As Father lay in bed, his wondering about what they had come for chased away all sleep. The hours of night passed slowly.

Before the sun rose, before the ground was white, all villagers were gathered for a meeting. This white man was different—his trunk was fat and his head was small, like the baobab tree. But his clothes and feet were the same. And his head was covered with the round white hat with the veranda.

The white man spoke through one of his black helpers. He had come for the water of a tree—only one kind of tree. His helpers would show the village men the kind of tree which had the water he wanted. They would show how to cut the tree so the water would run freely. Every village man was to return within two days with a gourd full of tree water.

People had many questions inside them. "What is this for?" "What is our pay?" "What will he do with the water?" "Will he make us carry it elsewhere?" But when they saw the big black men with fire sticks, they closed their mouths. Their questions remained inside them.

As Father worked in the forest to fill his gourd, one thing made him laugh inside. It was the shame of his black masters. This white man had not come to fulfill the promise. He had come to enslave them all. Father's black masters could no longer walk with their chests thrown high. Now their pride too was broken. They too were slaves, no higher than he. They quietly worked alongside him.

When the second day ended, the gourds were not full. The white man's law was too hard for them. They were trapped. Slinkingly, they returned to the village.

When they had all returned, they were made to gather in the great open space before the chief's hut. When the white man saw the gourds partly filled, he had anger, terrible anger of fire, anger which burned red in his face. His voice roared like that of a lion hunting prey. Our people's hearts split with fear; their bodies became weak as water.

"I had hoped you would be different from other black people," he shouted, his black helper turning the words around for us to understand. "But you are the same. You think I am playing. You think I give orders uselessly. You trample my words underfoot like dirt. Why do you not obey as human beings? It is because you are animals. All black men are useless animals. They are stupid as monkeys. Because you act like animals who don't hear, I must treat you as animals. I will do something bad. Very bad. I must do it so that you learn quickly and well. Then you will never shame my words again. You will bring me tree water rapidly. You will not complain."

He said something to his eight black servants standing near him. Six of them, with their fire sticks, surrounded the village people who were sitting on the ground. The two servants which remained began pulling children from the arms of their parents who held them. They took Disanka and Ditekemena and many others.

The children were thrown to the ground, at one place. Soon they were piled on top of each other. They screamed, and kicked their feet in the air. Ditekemena got up and tried to run to Father. She was caught and thrown with force to the ground again. Rage burned Father's insides like fire.

Then the two black servants got their fire sticks. They held them by the little ends and lifted them high over the children. Parents changed into stones, watching. Father saw the terrible fear in Ditekemena's eyes while she watched the stick come down to hit her. The sticks hit the children one time and another time and another time. Each time there were screams and the sounds of breaking bones. Rage made parents become crazy. They leaped forward and threw themselves down on top of their children. The fire sticks hit bodies of parents. They hit again and again. Then they stopped.

The affair was finished. Mother and Father lay on Disanka and Ditekemena. Happiness had disappeared forever. Father closed his eyes. He could not look upon the broken skulls spilling blood. He could not look upon the ground, wet and red with the blood of his seed. He cried aloud, his tears flowing as rivers of water. He cried until no strength remained; then he moaned. He did not feel the warm hands of tribemates who tried to comfort him. He heard none of their words. His mourning did not lessen the weight of grief within him.

With his mourning came the remembrance of his childhood, when he was free. A picture of that life stood with a picture of his life now. Surely there was no greater shame. Now this white man had arrived and destroyed the seed of their bodies. How could Mvidi Mukulu create a person who caused other people to suffer thus? What hope was left upon earth? Perhaps Mvidi Mukulu would show him kindness and take his life from off the earth.

But life would not leave him. No one was kind to take it from him. He opened his eyes. It was night. Friends tried to lift him. He refused. He was too weak to sit. He wanted to lie on the ground.

He could not die. He had to live. While he lived, he had to carry the griefs of life. He suffered all these griefs because he was a slave, first to black masters, now to white masters. He hated them. They made him as the dirt upon which he lay; even though an elephant trampled it, it could not complain. They would grind him as corn between millstones all his living days.

Was there nothing good which remained? Ditekemena. They took away her body, but the meaning of her name remained. He would hope. Hope would give him strength to work, hope would cause him to fight, hope would help him scheme until he found freedom.

Freedom. This was what he must live for. The thought filled him like hot medicine which began to heal his heart. When he found freedom, he could buy his own fire stick. He could protect his wife and children that Mvidi Mukulu might yet give them; he could protect them from the death he had just seen with his eyes. He could have his own home—his own field. He would rejoice with the things Mvidi Mukulu meant for all men to have. He could cause the stigma of slavery to disappear forever. He could be a man again, proud, strong, free, as his forefathers were.

The thought strengthened his heart. He hoped for freedom. He craved it as a man lost in a wilderness craves water. He craved it as a widow craves the love of her mate. This kind of craving never ends. He would find freedom someday. If he did not find freedom, he would die with the hope of it in his heart.

*   *   *

Don't kill a dog on the ground. The earth you walk on will hear the beating of the dog's tail. The earth will remember it. When the time is sufficient, the earth will curse you, and the dog will be avenged.

3

The white man got all the tree water his heart desired. He left. Father rejoiced. His tribemates rejoiced. Their masters rejoiced. Everybody rejoiced. They hoped the white man had gone as water down the river forever.

When a short time passed something else happened and their joy ended. Four strange black men arrived. They wore red hats which had no verandas. Their chests and waists were covered with cloth of the white man. They carried fire sticks. They told the chief to call the village people together. They had words to speak.

The hearts and minds of people refused the command. But slowly their bodies obeyed. They obeyed as goats being dragged by their tether ropes to be butchered. They gathered in the great open space before the hut of the village chief. Every person's face was changed by fear. The few people who remained with children held them tightly.

The chief told everyone to sit on the ground and listen to the words of the visitors. One strange black man stepped forward and spoke. A great white chief had arrived. He had come in a boat greater than our eyes had ever seen. He was living at the river village of Luaba.

He had not come to catch slaves or to get rubber water; he had come to teach black people his laws. These laws would stop people-stealing and children-killing and bring peace and happiness. But he must have workers to help him. Each chief was to send him four men. They would be paid

26

for their work. They would receive cloth to cover their bodies, and salt.

The village chief and his elders gathered to one side. They sat in a circle to discuss this affair.

"Look at the cunningness of the white man as he sets this new trap to catch men," said one. "Doesn't he know that animals learn to recognize traps which have caught their kin? If we are wise, we will evade it."

"Give a rat a grain of corn and he'll come hunting for your granary," said another.

"We know that the white man's mouth doesn't speak; it only eats," said another. "But if we refuse his word, what kind of trouble will catch us? He could send many men with fire sticks. They could sweep us off the earth forever, like wind sweeps the dust."

After these words, the men sat quietly. They frowned as they studied their problem. Then one of them spoke.

"We need not send our own people into the slavery of the white man," he said. "Do we not have slaves among us? Does the white man know whom we send him? Will he return to trouble us if those we send him work well? Let us send him four of our slaves. Then we will find out what this white man wants to do with people."

"This is good wisdom," they agreed.

"But who among us wants to lose slaves who work well for them?"

"We shall cast lots," the chief said. "Lots will show us which slaves are to be sent to the white man."

All the people silently watched the chief and elders in counsel. Then my father and three tribemates were called.

"You will arrange your affairs to leave," the chief said. "You will begin your journey in the morning. Your wives will go with you. You will go with the owners of the red hats to work for their white man."

When morning came, the four men and their wives departed. The journey did not cause them suffering. They were not tied. The strangers did not use their fire sticks.

But while their bodies suffered little, their minds suffered much. No white man ever brought peace and happiness; they brought torment and death. If only they would not trouble us with their affairs—if they would leave us alone— then we would know peace and happiness.

They arrived at the village of Luaba that same day. That night they ate well and slept in a large hut. Each day others arrived, until there were about a hundred. On the fifth day, the men with red hats and fire sticks took all of them to a very large hut. Father had never seen so great a hut. It had a long sloping roof and was surrounded by a wide veranda. It sat on a hillside near the river and was called a house. Father and the others were made to sit on the ground, their faces to the house, their backs to the big river.

Then from the house came a white man. He stood on steps that led up to the front veranda. He was not like a bamboo stalk, nor like the baobab tree. His body, covered with white cloth, was that of a strong man. He passed up my father in size only slightly. He spoke loudly in a tongue nobody understood. Black men with red hats turned the words around into tongues people could hear.

"White men with bad hearts have caused much suffering in your land," he said. "Do not think that all white men have evil hearts like those who have caused you to suffer. Among white men, as among your people, some hearts are bad, but many are good.

"News of your suffering has passed across the great water and reached the ears of all white men," he said. "My kingdom was chosen from among kingdoms to study the affair; it has sent me and many others to your land. It has sent us to stop the buying of people and to catch and punish those who cause people to suffer. It has sent us to establish laws. When these laws are established, all tribesmen will have their homes and gardens. All will sell and buy the things they desire. All will sit in peace. ·

"These are good things," he said. "But I cannot do them alone. Because of this, your chiefs sent you. You will be my helpers. You are not slaves. Each of you will till your garden. You will work for me. When each moon is finished, I will pay you. Your wages will be cloth for your bodies and salt to flavor your food.

"To arrange the bad matters in your land, I must be chief," he declared. "The words of a chief must be obeyed. Work hard and obey me well. You will be happy. You will be rewarded well. However, if you count my words as useless, if you try to flee, you will be punished. I am strong. People who have seen my strength with their eyes have named me Bula Matadi. Stay well."

Father did not believe most of what the white man said. Father knew a white man would not leave his kingdom across the great water to come to our land because he wanted to help us. Father knew well the paw of a lion. It was soft and warm until it could catch its prey, then came forth claws which grabbed and tore and held forever.

But Father would obey, because the paw was yet soft. He would work, for he wanted his own home and garden. He would work hard for one moon and see with his own eyes the white man's pay. He would not try to flee at this time. He remembered and feared the white man's name, Bula Matadi. It meant the crusher of stones.

Father built his hut. He and Mother planted their garden. Then he worked hard for Bula Matadi; he cleared land, planted gardens, helped build many huts and houses. He worked for Bula Matadi one moon. He saw the wages of his work. This was good. He had never before received wages for his work. He would not complain. A goat crying for its mother can carry no burden. He would carry his burden well. He worked for Bula Matadi another moon—for many moons—for moons sufficient for one year, for two years, for many years.

Father worked for Bula Matadi, but he did not understand him. He did not trust him. Like the children-killer, Bula Matadi had anger. It burned in his face, red like fire. It gave him a voice like the roar of a lion. It reminded Father of days he wanted to forget.

Bula Matadi beat tribesmen with the hippopotamus whip; sometimes they had done wrong, sometimes they had not. Bula Matadi sent his red-capped men with fire sticks to villages, where they took meat from the villagers and brought it to him. Sometimes Bula Matadi would take a daughter of one of his workmen—a girl with a well-formed body—to stay with him during the night. Father did not understand these things. He did not try to understand them. Who on earth could understand the customs of the white man? All his customs were upside down. Did even Mvidi Mukulu understand them?

Yet since Father had begun working for Bula Matadi, many affairs appeared which strengthened his heart.

Bula Matadi and his red-capped soldiers made war on a white man who was buying people. They caught him, tied him and put him in a big boat which took him down the river to the city of the big chief for judgment. Since that time, no white man had come hunting slaves or rubber water.

The soldiers of Bula Matadi caught and judged tribe leaders who stirred up people to fight. Thus people lived in peace. They tilled their fields. They traded things from their fields for things they needed.

Affairs of Father's home strengthened his heart. Before a

year of moons had passed, Mother bore my brother, Mutombo. Then she bore my sister, Ndaya, and then me, Mulumba. For many moons dreams of how Disanka and Ditekemena died caused my parents to suffer. Now, because other children were born, these dreams began to disappear.

But above everything else, Father's heart was strengthened by affairs of his work. When a moon finished, Bula Matadi never failed to pay him. Always, this was a day of great joy. Father earned enough cloth to cover the bodies of Mother and the children well; some cloth even remained. He earned enough salt for their food, and more. Salt or cloth which remained was used to buy a chicken or fresh meat from the forest or a cooking pot. Hold fast to what you have earned, the elders say, or you'll be forever chasing a dream.

Bula Matadi saw the hard work of Father and rewarded him. First he placed him over eight workmen. Later, Bula Matadi gave him a red hat and a fire stick and made him a soldier. Thus Father got more pay. He also got his portion of fresh meat from animals taken in the villages.

To Father, the day they paid him was a sign. It showed him that the shame of slavery was beginning to remain behind him. Little by little, the bird builds its nest, he told himself. When he was placed over other men, he rejoiced. He had authority in his hands. There was no one here to remind him he had been a slave. He was becoming a man again. He was proud.

When he was made a soldier, he began to long for the day when he would be sent with other soldiers to the village where he had worked so many years for nothing. They would go with their fire sticks to the chief and his elders. They would demand from them a tax of live animals. Those who had enslaved him would bow in submission. Those who once laughed at him would now sit in shame. The soldiers

31

would bring the animals to Bula Matadi and slay and eat them. To Father, this meat would pass all others in tasting good.

Father did not like Bula Matadi. But he liked very much the power of things and authority he received from **Bula Matadi**; it tasted sweet as the juice of sugar cane. He would work hard. He would get more things and more authority. He would build a larger hut, perhaps a house. He would barter some of his things for animals which could reproduce and bring him wealth. He would use his fire stick with the greatest of wisdom and be a good soldier.

Perhaps this was the way Mvidi Mukulu was arranging for him to recover all that he'd lost because of the evils of the white man. Perhaps in this way the vow that started inside him when his body lay on soil wet with his children's blood was being fulfilled. Was the earth beginning to avenge him of the wrongs he had suffered? After many days, would this path he had begun truly lead him to freedom?

Then another white man arrived. He came in a big boat on the river. His wife was with him. She was white as he, with long hair, straight and fine. Father reminded himself of the acts of the white men he had known—the buyer of people, the children-killer and Bula Matadi. When he heard why this white man had come, he couldn't believe it. This white man must be the greatest deceiver of them all. He said he had come to teach about Mvidi Mukulu.

✿ ✿ ✿

If a borrowed millstone grinds your flour, care for it well, that it grind for you many days.

4

Here I begin the footprints of my own memory. I, Mulumba, remember when the new white man built his compound on the other side of the river. I remember how every day Bula Matadi would send workmen across the river to help the new white man cut down jungle, clear the ground, build his huts. I remember workmen returning with strange stories.

They said this white man had magic medicines which he guarded in a hut. He said these medicines would make great sores disappear and cause new life to return into dying bodies; they could overpower evil spirits who cursed us with sickness.

I remember Father's doubts. "Bula Matadi sends his workmen to build the compound of the new white man," he said. "This shows that they are people of one heart. Two white men can fit together easily, but for them to fit with us is another matter. Two faces can see each other, but a hip and a back are from two bodies.

"This white man is the same as the others," Father said. "They all have the same customs. If their Mvidi Mukulu accepts the things they do on earth, He is different from the Mvidi Mukulu we worship. He is a stranger to us. His laws are not straight. We do not need Him."

Father also doubted the affair of the white man's medicine. "How can a stranger from across the great water understand our sicknesses?" he asked. "We have had our own doctors from the beginning. Have they learned nothing all these years they have been among us? Do they not use herbs to heal our sicknesses? Do they not drive evil spirits from bodies which suffer? Do they not expose sorcerers? It is the will of Mvidi Mukulu that when a man's days are sufficient, he dies. It is not the will of Mvidi Mukulu that a man live forever."

One afternoon Bula Matadi called Father.

"Tomorrow you will go with ten men across the river," he said. "You will help the new white man. Guard your men. See that they work well."

Father had struck his foot onto good luck. Now he would see with his own eyes the affairs of this white man.

Our hearts were suspended the whole day Father was gone while we waited for his return. After supper we sat by the fire and Father told us strange new things.

"This white man wears clothes like all the other white men," Father said. "He wears the round white hat with the veranda; his house is big. In many things he appears like all white men. But his body is small and his voice is weak.

"His wife is strange-looking, as people told us," Father said. "She works at the hut which guards their medicines. She did not have many people to heal for they brought her only a few worthless people, whose sicknesses have already made them as dead.

"The white man brought a black helper with him who turns the white man's words around for us to understand," Father related. "The white man ordered me to build him a house that is not closed in by walls. He said he will gather children into this house to teach them. He wants to teach them to make paper leaves talk."

Father worked for this white man a half moon of days. For Father's men, these were days of work; for Father, they were days of watching. By the time they had finished the

34

work, Father had seen many new affairs—affairs which he spoke into our ears.

"The white man carries a bundle of leaves with marks on them. He says these leaves talk to him. He says they tell him the laws of Mvidi Mukulu," Father said. "He teaches the laws to the sick who come for healing. He wants to teach these laws to our children. He says he will teach us all to accept the laws of his Mvidi Mukulu. This we shall see."

"Are the people healed?" we asked.

"Some get better; some die."

"Does he have a fire stick?"

"We have not seen it; perhaps it is in his house."

"Does he take a black girl to sleep with him at night?"

"No," Father said. "He has his own wife."

"Does his face redden with anger? Does he use the whip?"

"No. His voice is weak. I have not seen his anger. His body is small. A jackal cannot have the anger of a lion."

Then Father was sent to other places to work. He told us what he learned at these places, but Mutombo and I wanted to learn more affairs from across the river.

Soon a few of our playmates began to go hear the teaching of the white man. They liked it and went days following after each other. Every afternoon Mutombo and I felt our hearts tugging to go to our friends' houses to see them. We wanted to learn what had passed that day.

"Is he like all white men?" we asked.

"Some of his affairs are the same; some are different."

"What is his name?"

"He calls himself the speaker of Mvidi Mukulu. We call him Speaker."

"He promised to teach you how to make paper leaves talk. Has he fulfilled his promise?"

"He says this must come afterwards," the children said.

"He asks us names of things and writes talking marks onto paper. He is teaching us talking marks for our numbers. Watch." A playmate straightened his finger and made strange marks in the dust.

"Are many children going?"

"At first there were few. Then Speaker began other wisdom. Children who come every day for five days are given a spoon of salt. Children who come every day for twenty days are given a piece of soap. Now the children are many."

"Does he have anger? Does he use the whip?"

"He has anger, but not of fire. One child did a shameful deed. Speaker whipped him with a vine whip."

But the vine whip of Speaker did not scare away our playmates. They went across the river many days—days of many moons. Their hunger for the affairs of Speaker grew. Mutombo and I saw that this hunger was catching our hearts also.

"May we go with our playmates across the river tomorrow?" we asked Father one evening.

"Why do you want to go across the river?"

"To hear the teaching of the white man."

"These children who have gone many days, what have they learned?"

"They have learned to write talking marks for numbers. They showed us. They wrote them on the ground."

"Do you need marks on the ground to count? Can't you count on your fingers? Is it good wisdom to teach an antelope how to run?"

"But the white man is paying children to come. He gives them salt and soap," Mutombo said.

"After the prairie fox is trapped, is he still happy for the meat which baited him?" Father asked. "Don't we have all the salt and soap we need here in the house? Where are the children he has taught to make paper leaves talk? Have you not heard that he uses the whip, like all white men? There is word that children disappear from time to time. A white man caused me to lose two children. No matter how great their cunningness, they will cause me to lose no more. They are like leopards. On the outside is beauty; on the inside is war. You will not go across the river tomorrow, or another day. The affair is finished."

Father had refused with strength. His heart wanted to refuse forever. Then came an affair which made us very sad. This new sadness made us forget the desire to go with our playmates across the river.

Sickness caught our sister Ndaya. Her body was hot for many days. She could not eat. She only drank water. Her body became weak. Mother held her in her arms during the hours of daylight; Father held her during the hours of night. Many times she moaned, as a little animal dying of its wounds. We did not sleep well.

Father called a doctor—an old man known to be wise in the affairs of our sicknesses. Father paid him well. The doctor used many herbs from the jungle and with some he made bitter water for Ndaya to drink, with others he rubbed her body. Her illness remained.

The doctor said Ndaya was sick because of the anger of ancestral spirits. So Father gave him a chicken and he offered it as a blood sacrifice to appease the anger of the spirits. The illness of Ndaya remained.

One night when Mutombo and I went to bed Father was seated at the fire outside. He was holding Ndaya while she cried weakly. The hearts of all of us were filled with sadness. Mother sat with Father.

"Ndaya is no better."

"Yes," Father replied.

"Her sickness is stronger than the herbs can heal."

"Yes."

"The ancestral spirits are satisfied."

"Yes," Father answered.

"Do you have other wisdom to help us?"

"No."

"Is there not other medicine we can give her?"

"What other kind of medicine can we give her?"

"Is there not medicine across the river?"

Father paused and then spoke with anger. "The white man killed two of my girl children when they were strong. What would he do with this one when she is weak?"

"But you said some of the people the white man treated died and some got well. If we do nothing, Ndaya will leave us forever."

"How will our ancestral spirits feel if we seek the help of strangers?" Father asked. "Will they not recompense us with evil? Would you so offend our native doctors? For revenge, would they not curse us? When sickness catches us in the days ahead, would our ancestral spirits want to help us? Don't speak foolishly. If our daughter died across the river, it would be the fault of the white man. It is better that she stay here. Then if she dies, we will know it was the will of Mvidi Mukulu."

Mother did not answer.

The doctor would not be shamed that he had failed. He visited other parents and found that other children were sick also. One evening he called all parents to meet together.

"A sickness of children is troubling us much these days," he told them. "I have tried all medicines of herbs. They have failed. I have offered sacrifices to appease the anger of ancestral spirits. The sicknesses still trouble us. There remains one path for us. The sickness is caused by someone among us. We must find who it is and give him the trial cup. Unless we find who it is, the sickness he is causing could kill all your children."

38

Parents agreed that the one troubling us must be found. Together they gathered animals sufficient to pay the doctor for the work he was about to do. He called two men who also had much wisdom in matters of our sicknesses and sat on the ground, one of his friends on either side of him. One of them played a small drum. They both sang. The doctor closed his eyes to think deeply. He began to sway from side to side, as if sleeping, sitting. He was talking with departed spirits. They revealed to him the name of him who was causing the sickness.

The doctor called the name of the guilty one. He was a young man with strength, the son of Father's friend.

They found the young man and brought him inside the circle of people. They made him sit down while the doctor and his helpers prepared the trial cup. They made the young man drink it. If he was innocent, it would not trouble him. If he was guilty, he would die. In a few minutes he fell to the ground rolling this way and that, clutching at his stomach. His face was twisted in suffering and his body gave forth sweat as raindrops. In a short time he died.

In the days that followed, the sickness of some of the children left them, but the sickness of Ndaya remained.

"See how her sickness remains while others have recovered?" the doctor said to Father one evening. "This proves the sickness is now her fault; it is no longer to be blamed on someone else."

"Why does she not get well?" Father asked.

"Her sickness is caused by an evil spirit which lives inside her," the doctor said.

"How shall we help her?" Father asked.

"We shall open her flesh and let the evil spirit escape; then the child will recover."

Mother looked at Father quickly. His face was changed with the suffering of his heart. He thought for a time. Then he looked at the doctor and said, "We will wait with this affair. We will wait until I return from work tomorrow afternoon. Then I will answer you."

When the doctor left, Father told us children to go to bed. While we lay in bed, we heard the noise of someone catching a rooster. It squawked one time and then there was quietness. Then we heard Father praying at the miabi tree:

> O great Lord in the sky,
> Show-er of love,
> Spirit-Creator of our forefathers,
> To You, the darkness of tomorrow is bright
>   as when the sun is high.
> Even the spirits are Your slaves.
> We have said everything;
> We have done everything;
> We have seen no results.
> Our hearts are dry.
> This sickness is so great, even the hills
>   have finished their strength.
> Only You remain.
> Why don't You help us in our troubles?
> We have suffered too much.
> If this sickness comes from Your finger,
> Free us from it.
> If You want to kill,
> Then kill me.
> For we have suffered too much.

When morning came, Father looked at Ndaya. Her sickness was the same. Father went to work. When he had left, Mother spoke.

"Mulumba, you remain here at the hut all day. If your father returns, tell him I have gone with Ndaya to the hut of a friend, tell him I will return in a short time. Mutombo, you will go with me."

40

"Where are you going?" I asked.

"I am going across the river," Mother replied.

Mother returned when the sun was straight up. When the sun went down, Ndaya was a little better. When Father saw this, he told the native doctor to wait.

That night Ndaya slept for the first time in many nights. When morning came, she was hungry. Father was surprised and very happy.

"Perhaps she is better because the evil spirit has left her," he said to Mother.

"No," Mother replied.

"Why is she better?"

"She is better because of medicine."

"What kind of medicine?" Father asked.

Mother waited a moment, then she said, "Medicine from across the river."

Father looked at the ground hard. He looked for a long time. He said nothing.

When Father went to work the next day, Mother went across the river with Ndaya. This happened for many days. Father asked Mother no more questions for Ndaya was getting strong again and Father was happy.

More days passed. Father watched Ndaya become strong like she was before. One evening, after he had eaten supper, he called Mutombo and me to the fire. We sat down. He spoke.

"I have warned you many times of the badness of the white man. He is like a laughing dog. It laughs as it growls. But we have found help in the white man's different kinds of things. Mvidi Mukulu would not refuse for us to have things which make greater our happiness upon earth; He created all things. This is why I work for Bula Matadi. The things we receive from our work help us forget the shameful affairs which have remained behind us. You can't catch a good reputation like you can a grasshopper; you must work for it. For this reason I work harder than others. I work patiently. Those who have patience won't need to eat green fruit. We are progressing. People are forgetting old affairs. Now when they see me, they count me a person of honor.

"In the moon behind us, three new men began working for Bula Matadi," Father said. "They are young. They make number marks on paper. When the moon finished, Bula Matadi gave them more pay than any of us. He told us, 'Those who know marks on paper help me exceedingly.'

"I do not want you to remain behind others. I don't want you to fail to have the abundance of things which will increase your happiness upon earth. Eat while the pot is unbroken, they say, drink while the streams have water. It is time for you to begin eating and drinking. It is time for you to learn things which will help you in your journeys upon earth. As I have worked hard, you must work hard.

"When you have learned well, you will have power within you to surpass many others," Father explained. "As they count me a person of honor, they will count you persons of much honor. You will erase from the minds of people memories of shame. You will restore to our forefathers the glory they had. The name of our tribe will be a name of honor again.

"To accomplish this, you must begin to learn now," Father said. "When the sun comes up tomorrow, you will go across the river."

❉   ❉   ❉

Who is it that does great things? Mvidi Mukulu, doing bit by bit, always succeeds. The termite is like Him; little by little, it eats a house.

5

Mutombo and I rejoiced with joy that reached from heaven to earth. That night we lay in our beds, but sleep fled from us. The affairs that began tomorrow would change us into different people. We waited for morning, our hearts trembling. Ndaya had suffered much but her sickness had softened Father's heart.

When morning came Mother cut two new pieces of cloth for us. We wrapped them around our waists and went to our playmates' hut. They took us across the river.

The first day we had much fear. We had not yet seen a white man closely. The helper of Speaker asked us our names and then made talking marks on a leaf of paper in his hand. Then he took us into the teaching house where there were perhaps twenty children, sitting like little blackbirds in a nest, expecting to be fed. They gave us places to sit.

Suddenly Speaker entered. My heart wanted to stand still. He was small, as we had heard. First he said we would together talk to Mvidi Mukulu. He told us to lower our heads and cover our eyes. I was afraid to cover my eyes well. I feared he would do something bad to us while we could not see. I watched him between my fingers. His eyes were tightly closed. I could not see the Spirit to whom he was talking.

I do not remember what Speaker taught us that day. My ears heard the noise of his words, but there was no room in my mind to receive them. I was fearful, as a hungry dog which has come to the house of a stranger to beg. My mind

43

was full of what Father had told us about white men: "The white man has caused us much suffering. He is a stranger to us. His laws are not straight. Beware of his cleverness to deceive."

What I saw that day, and following days, taught me that if Speaker was deceiving the class children, he was deceiving them well. They did not fear him. Their hearts accepted him. Thus there was room in their minds to receive the affairs he taught them.

How could I learn from Speaker if I did not accept him? Father had told us to learn all the affairs of the white man that would increase our happiness upon earth. Little by little, the hearts of Mutombo and me began to trust Speaker. Then our minds accepted rapidly the affairs he taught us. Father's other words bound us like a law: "You must work hard. Thus you will become people of honor. You will erase from the minds of others memories of shame." Thus we worked, and we began to pass others in learning.

After many days another white man and his wife arrived. He was as tall as Father, and heavier. His wife was as tall as he, but thin. We children were given hoes and knives to clear ground for his compound. We tilled ground for his garden. My body was taller and stronger than those of many other children my age. I worked hard.

One day a soldier with men arrived. They cut sticks from the jungle and dug clay from the river bank. They set the sticks closely together in the ground and packed between them wet clay, making a house wall. We carried great bunches of long thin grass from the prairie, which they tied onto the roof. Thus they built the house of the new white man. They built a stick fence and a small hut for his animals. One day, when class was finished, Speaker called Mutombo and me.

"I have watched how you study and how you work," he

44

said. "You work well. You learn rapidly. I want you to be helpers in the compound of the new white man. Teach him and his wife the words of your language. Do the different kinds of work they tell you to do. If you guard yourselves well, this work will bring you great reward."

So we were taken to the new white man's house. This white man was to be over the affairs of the teaching house; thus Speaker could do the work of Mvidi Mukulu. We named him Teacher-Revealer. His teaching would reveal to us many new things. We named his wife Helper.

The voice of Teacher was strong. When he spoke, I remembered the voice of Bula Matadi and fear wanted to catch me. But he spoke little with his voice, because he knew few words. He spoke much with his hands.

Teacher took us to the stick fence and showed us six goats. His voice and his hands showed us that Mutombo was to take care of his goats and tend to his yard and garden. Then he took me inside the house. He showed me that I was to work there, with his wife, Helper. He told us to come to work when the ground began to get white in the morning. Then he said, "Go well."

Mutombo and I were very happy. Our hearts skipped like those of young antelopes playing in the sunlight. We ran to the river and all the way home. We wanted to tell Mother and Father the good news.

When they heard, Mother's face brightened like sunshine, but Father's became cloudy like a sky that may bring storm. "Is that white man going away someday or has he come to stay?" he asked.

"He has come to stay, like Bula Matadi," we assured him. "He brought many boxes; he has filled the house with his things. They are things of one who sits, not of one who is traveling."

"It is not good for both of you to be in the hands of one

white man," he said. "I do not want some useless vagabond to cause me to lose my two boys."

"It would be good for you to watch Speaker and Teacher for many days as we have," I said. "You would understand that their hearts are not like that of the rubber-juice hunter."

"The animals play innocently while the hunters encircle them with their nets," said Father. "Try to learn more rapidly. Stay across the river only until you learn the number marks well; then you can get work with good pay. Leave before the net closes and you cannot escape forever."

Mutombo, my elder brother, spoke carefully. "Father, you told us how the white man's things have helped us—his salt—his cloth—his medicine. You have seen how the white man's wisdom of number marks has given young men authority greater than yours. We heard your words, that you did not want us to remain behind others. We heard the law you bound us with—to learn all we can so that we can surpass others and bring honor to the name of our tribe again.

"But how can we fulfill your hope if you give us other laws which tie us as vines?" Mutombo asked. "Does not the fast running dog catch the animal? We are beginning to run fast now. We learn wisdom of the white man in the teaching house with children. Now we have been chosen to learn wisdom of the white man inside his own house. Haven't we struck a foot of good luck? Isn't it good that we are going forward? Shall we not fulfill your hope in fewer days?"

Father's clouded face looked hard at the ground. A time passed. Then he looked at us and said, "A fast running dog is good, but the dog with all legs and no head runs too fast and leaves the animal behind. If you learn many things and by your alertness escape the net, you will bring us glory. If the net catches you because you are running too fast and you are taken away forever, shame and sorrow will bury me in the ground. Don't run too fast. Be as alert as the antelope who has heard sounds she doesn't yet understand. Don't get caught by lust for the white man's things. Stick yourselves to these laws. While both of you are under one white man, my heart will not rest well. I fear trouble will catch you."

The affairs of the new white man were as strange as new food in our mouths—food hard for us to eat. But we ate them. Mutombo learned to herd and feed the goats. He learned which tender green garden plants were to be made to grow and which were useless and to be pulled and discarded.

I learned to make fire inside the iron kitchen box. I learned to pour hot food from pots into glass dishes without burning myself. I learned to carry the dishes one following another to the table, without breaking them, as Helper desired. I learned to wash dishes in water that burned my hands. I learned to sweep the floor and arrange the house. Though my heart told me that some of the things I did were foolish, I obeyed and did them. Helper wanted it this way.

While we learned, we marveled at the white man's customs. He stole milk from a mother goat and put it into his own stomach. He ate things with odors so bad my stomach turned around. He and Helper slept on a great soft pillow on four legs, a pillow which passed them in length.

We tried hard to learn the wisdom of the white man, but sometimes he made us do things we wanted to refuse. Teacher wanted us to wear trousers. We rebelled. We had always found loincloths sufficient. Teacher troubled us much with this affair. One day he spoke to me strongly with his voice and his hands.

"Helper has made you a pair of trousers. You must learn to wear them," he said. "When Bula Matadi comes here to eat dinner, we don't want him to see a heathen serving our table."

"Heathen" is a bad word. I did not understand how being a heathen stopped when one put on trousers, but I still feared to disobey the word of the white man. I took the trousers and went into a little room he showed me. I closed the door. I took off my loin cloth. To put on the trousers was a hard affair; one foot sent toward the river, the other sent toward the hill. Much shame caught me, without my loincloth. I did not feel the trousers covered me well. I wore them while I was inside the house, to make the white man happy. I did not leave the house with them on for my classmates would have laughed at me, without mercy. I wondered if my ancestral spirits saw me walking around without a loincloth. Some of the wisdom of the white man passed up our minds to understand.

Moons passed. Bit by bit we became accustomed to the white man's ways. Slowly, others learned to wear trousers without shame. In sufficient time, Mutombo and I knew every corner of the white man's compound. The problem of how to learn faster kept troubling us although Father's strong words of warning about the white man's things began to remain far behind.

I learned number marks quickly, but only after a year of moons did paper begin to tell me other things. I was not happy with my slowness of reading. Like this, the patience of Father would become finished. Many years would pass before I could fulfill our hopes. I must find a way to learn to read more rapidly. As our elders say, Others are going; move along yourself. If you don't, you'll remain behind forever.

One day I struck a good foot of luck with a boy named Kabeya. He was in the class ahead of me. I was telling him how learning to read was troubling me.

48

"Two walking together can give each other wisdom," he said. "Do you have many papers to read?"

"I have only the reading papers of my class," I replied.

"You'll learn the strength of your hoe by using it much," he said. "And you will learn to read rapidly only by reading much."

"Where can I find other papers to read?" I asked.

"I have so many reading papers that I cannot read them all. Begging is not stealing," he said.

"I beg of you to loan me some that you don't need," I said.

He gave me four reading sheets. I thanked him.

Kabeya replied, "Our forefathers said, Give something back to the one who gave to you."

"What are you asking for?"

"Any little thing you find at hand which would make a person happy," he answered.

"I am not an owner of many things," I replied. "Where could I get something to make you happy?"

"Do you not work in the house of the white man?" Kabeya asked. "Is his house not filled up with things? Does not the many-ness of his things pass up his wisdom to remember them all? Have you never made yourself happy with a few of his little things?"

I wanted to say that I had guarded myself well, but Kabeya was older than I. The wisdom of his questions shamed me. I did not answer.

"Does the white man not tell us he has only come to help us?" Kabeya continued. "Has he not said many times that he loves us? We have few things. He has exceedingly many things. Is it not wrong for him to keep to himself things which we need? Why should he refuse us such things to help us? Why should he be angry with us for having the things we need, if he loves us? Mulumba, you want to progress rapidly. You have a foot of good luck because you work in the house of the white man. Heap firewood on your coals while firewood is near or you will never build your fire. If you want to help me along you will have all the reading papers your heart longs for."

I returned to the white man's house. I took Kabeya's papers and his words with me. His words made my heart pound. It was true that I found myself among the things of Teacher—things too many for him to remember. Then I heard a voice in my heart. It said that Teacher was happy with my work, he gave me pay of salt and soap. I should not hunt trouble that might make me lose the good things I had.

I studied the papers of Kabeya, reading them many times. He said he had many more. They were from the class ahead of me. With the help of these papers I could pass up all others in my class.

A different voice spoke in my heart. It reminded me that I wanted more than anything else to get ahead rapidly. A way of getting ahead rapidly was near me. Only a foolish leopard would refuse to grab prey that was beside him. Would it not be foolish for me to refuse the wisdom of Kabeya and stay behind? Had not Father said to use the things of the white man which would increase our happiness on earth? Had he not bound me with a law to rise rapidly above others and thus restore honor to our tribe? Had he not said we should be wise, so as to flee the trap before it closed upon us?

The words of Kabeya were good. If Teacher learned we were using his things and he became angry with us, this would prove that he did not love us. This would reveal that he had come among us for some other purpose. Then we would be able to escape his trap in time.

I had finished studying Kabeya's four papers. One day

when I was alone in Helper's kitchen, I tasted sugar. It was as sweet as forest honey. Could I take some? Where would I put it, so no one could see? Truly, trousers are better than loincloths for this one thing—they have pockets. I wrapped some sugar in a large tree leaf, tucked it into my trouser pocket and went to see Kabeya.

Kabeya was happy. He loaned me more papers. I was happy. We did this many times, telling no one. Thus I learned many new things. I began passing up other children in my class. I progressed well.

One day I went into the yard to talk with Mutombo. He was seated behind a tree, reading a paper. It was a paper from the class ahead of me. I had already studied it. I asked him where he got it.

"From a friend," he said.

"Can you get some for me?" I asked.

"Does a friend help you for nothing?" he replied.

"Do you pay your friend?" I asked.

"The custom is to give something to the one who gave you."

"We are children of one mother. What do you pay him with?" I asked.

"I'm building my fire with firewood that is near me," he answered.

"Is the name of your friend Kabeya?" I asked.

"How did you know?" he asked with surprise.

"Kabeya knows many proverbs. He has been giving me papers for many days. I have already studied that one. I give him sugar."

"I give him a bit of salt from the sack in the goat shed," Mutombo said. "Kabeya has tricked us with his cleverness. Why should he receive pay of both salt and sugar for the same reading paper?"

Beginning then Mutombo and I shared papers; Kabeya

51

was paid once. Two boys from the same mother are clever to practice mischief. As the elders say, Let us two share our banana happily together; if a third one comes he'll say it is green. Thus Mutombo and I ate our banana together. We did thus for many days. We no longer thought about being happy. We only thought about working hard.

One day after class I did my work in the house rapidly. I went to sit with Mutombo to study new papers Kabeya had given us the day before. Teacher came from the teaching house. He called us. We went into the house. He and Helper were seated. Their faces were cloudy. Suddenly I remembered the day Father's face looked like a sky that was bringing storm and I remembered the words he had spoken: "It is not good for both of you to be in the hands of the same white man. I fear some bad affair will catch you." When I remembered, terrible fear caught me. I tried to lock it inside my heart. I tried to make my face appear brave.

"Are you guarding the goats well these days?" Teacher asked Mutombo.

"Yes, I am guarding them well," Mutombo replied.

"Are you guarding the shed well?" he asked.

"Yes, I guard it well," Mutombo replied.

"Are you sure no strangers enter the shed?" he asked.

"There is no stranger who enters the shed," Mutombo replied. "I guard it well."

"Thus you are the person who is taking salt from the bag," Teacher said.

"Why would I take salt from the bag?" Mutombo asked.

"I laid the tin cup in the salt in a manner I know. The cup has been moved. Salt has been taken. The top part of the bag is disarranged. You have said no stranger enters the goat shed. Thus you are guilty."

Mutombo hung his head. He said nothing. His shame was great.

Then the man with the hunting bow pointed his arrow at me. I could not flee.

"Mulumba, the smile of your early days has disappeared. What affair is troubling you? Do you guard the kitchen well?"

I could not say I didn't guard it well; they would chase me from my work and find one who did guard it well. If I answered, "Yes, I guard it well," I knew I was in the path of springing my own trap. While I struggled to escape, Teacher spoke again.

"Why are you taking sugar from the kitchen?"

"Why would I want to take your sugar?" I asked slinkily.

"Helper has marked the level of sugar in the can many times," he replied. "Many times sugar has been taken."

Our guilt covered us with shame, shame as the licking of feet. I looked at the face of Helper. I had never seen a face so sad. It made my insides sick.

The face of Teacher became darker with storm.

"Go to the village," he ordered. "Helper and I will think about this affair tonight. We will decide what to do with you. Return tomorrow morning."

Mutombo and I left, covered with shame. We walked home. We spoke nothing to each other. At home, Mother was preparing supper. Its odor made our stomachs sick. We ate little. We did not sit with Father at the fire, as was our custom. We wanted to go to bed.

"Has some sickness caught you?" he asked.

"No."

"Has some affair caught you?"

"No," we lied.

"Why are you going to bed at one time with the chickens?" he asked.

"We did much hard work today; our bodies are tired," Mutombo said. We went into our hut.

* * *

He who hunts a short path through the jungle will be eaten by the evil spirits. He who follows the long prairie path, when the time is sufficient, will arrive.

6

I went to bed, but I did not sleep. These affairs crushed me like the pestle crushes a palm nut in the mortar. My mind tortured me without rest. Only one person on this earth could teach me the wisdom I needed to find happiness on earth. This was the white man across the river. He had accepted me. I was learning well. I was going forward. I had laid hold of the hip meat of an antelope; then, like a fool, I lusted for its tail. The words of Kabeya and the pockets of the white man's trousers made me stumble. I took things of others. I stole, like a thief. This one foolish deed destroyed all faith Teacher had in me. I had ruined everything.

I had to return tomorrow morning. How do white men punish thieves? I remember how our forefathers punished them—they burned off their fingers. Thieves carried the symbol of theft to their graves. Then I remembered the rumor which made Father fear to send us across the river: "There is word that children disappear from time to time." Is this why they had disappeared? No, I would not go see Teacher in the morning. I would never go across the river again. Father had said, "If you are taken away, shame and sorrow will bury me in the ground."

I would stay at home tomorrow. Then the white man would not consume me with lion anger, his face burning red as fire. I would stay with Father and Mother. My affairs across the river were finished.

Then what would I tell Father in the morning? Could I lie again, as I had already done today? My lie might cover the affair for tomorrow and for the next day. But what about all the days ahead of me? Tell a bird a secret and it will fly away, they say. Tell it to a hen and she will cackle. This was not a flying-away secret. This was a secret of home. The hen would cackle. Soon everybody would know.

Then I must tell Father the truth.

When he hears the truth, what will he do? He had sent us across the river bound by his laws: that we work as hard as he had, that we guard ourselves well and not get into trouble with the white man's things. We were to gain for ourselves more honor than he had gained, we were to restore to the name of our tribe glory again, lifting it forever above memories of shame.

How has such a shameful deed caught me? Now I was the foolish dog. I'd run so fast, the animal had stayed behind. This shame would also fall upon Father—shame which would erase honor he had worked many years to earn—the honor that had begun to make him a proud man again.

How could I tell him what I had done? I had done across the river the very things he had warned us not to do. I had betrayed him and all he had entrusted me with. I could not face Father. I could not tell him. This burden passed up my strength to carry it. Was there no way to keep this shame from catching him?

We could run away. Yes, Mutombo. Let's run away. We can leave while it is yet dark. Then Father will never know.

Where shall we go? Where could we go? This is our village. We know no other village. Unless the soldiers of Bula Matadi were near, strange villagers would make us their slaves. This would send us back to follow the footprints of Grandfather going into slavery. This thought brought blackness which made me fear exceedingly.

If we tried to hide in the jungle, Teacher would tell Bula Matadi that we had stolen and fled. Bula Matadi would send his soldiers to find us. They would catch us and bring us to Bula Matadi for judgment. There, tied as animals awaiting slaughter, Teacher would come and burn us with his eyes.

Father had said a bad affair would catch us. This was it. Why hadn't we agreed with Father and stayed out of the white man's house? It would have been better for me to never have gone across the river. I should have been happy to sit at our hut and learn to work with my hands—work that is clean and honest.

But those days had passed, and now trouble had caught me. I could not see Teacher face to face. I could not stay at our house. I could not run away. It would be better for me to die. Yes, this would give me happiness.

Would I truly find happiness in death? Where would this happiness come from, when sin had made my heart black as charcoal? I remembered when I was a little child, when the moon made the ground white between the huts and I jumped and played in its light. Even when my heart was clean I had wondered about the Son of Mvidi Mukulu.

I was no happy child now. Fear had swallowed me up, and the Son of Mvidi Mukulu seemed far away. Why had I forgotten about Him? Why had I stopped searching for Him? When Speaker told us of Him in class across the river, why had I stuffed my ears? Father had told me His laws. Why had I broken them? I had forgotten about Mvidi Mukulu for many days. I could not die. I had not arranged myself to meet Mvidi Mukulu. I was afraid.

But my heart yearned to know Him. Perhaps He could take my sin away. Perhaps He could give me again the joy and happiness which I had as a child, when I danced in the moonlight. Where could I find answers to these questions? That Book. The Book of Mvidi Mukulu which is across the river. There I would find the answers. I could not find rest for my insides until I learned the affairs of that Book.

Teacher knows Mvidi Mukulu. Does his Mvidi Mukulu whiten hearts like the moon whitens the earth? If so, then perhaps Teacher would not consume me with his anger. He said he loves us. If he would let me speak, I would tell him I had been stubborn and foolish as a billy goat. I would confess that I had stuffed my ears to not hear the affairs of the Book. I would beg of him in the name of Mvidi Mukulu to cover my sin. I would beg of him to give me a tiny place of love in his heart. I would promise him that if I failed again, he could drive me away forever. But if Teacher had the anger of Bula Matadi, I would suffer. I might die. I might never see Mother and Father again forever.

I waited for morning. I did not know what it would bring, but I would go across the river.

Mutombo and I arrived at Teacher's house like all days. I started the fire. Helper came into the kitchen. She said nothing. I placed dishes of eating-things on the table. Teacher sat reading a book. He said nothing. I asked myself, "Do they have hearts to forget?"

When they finished eating, Teacher called Mutombo and me. They had not forgotten. Fear made my knees like water; I could not stand well. As the chipmunk fastens his eyes to the lion, hoping to escape his pounce, so I burned my eyes watching Teacher.

"Helper and I have not yet learned many words in your language," Teacher said, keeping anger inside him. "We have learned words of the kitchen, of the path, of the garden. Because of the affairs of yesterday, we are with much sadness. Our hearts are weak. Now I want to speak other words to you. I will try to speak the affairs of Mvidi Mukulu."

He would not first speak of punishment. He would speak of Mvidi Mukulu. I hoped exceedingly that his Mvidi Mukulu agreed with the Mvidi Mukulu of my Father. If so, we might escape. We might remain alive. We might not be branded with a symbol of thievery which would stay with us all our days. Could we strike such a foot of good luck?

Teacher hunted for more words. He said, "In the village of Mvidi Mukulu there is happiness forever. On earth some men kill, lie and steal. Men whose hearts are caught in sins cannot sit with Mvidi Mukulu. They cannot live in His village. He will chase them away. They will be punished for their bad affairs forever."

My heart, with its bad affairs, was wailing with sadness within me. My eyes, though standing still, were spilling water down my face.

"Mvidi Mukulu does not want to punish people," Teacher spoke slowly. "He wanted to show people His love. Therefore He sent His Son upon earth. He arranged a way to forgive people if they are truly sorry. Then their sin is covered. When they die they go to sit in the village of Mvidi Mukulu forever."

Teacher looked at us quietly.

"Your faces are sad," he said. "Perhaps you are sad because of your sin. Perhaps you are sad because we caught you. We do not know. Your work will show us. Are you sad because of your sin? Then your work will be good. Helper and I will be happy again. Our hearts will be strengthened. Are you sad because we caught you? Then you will steal again, and we will catch you again. Then here, at the mission post, you will have bad names. Your work with us will be finished forever. You will show us what you want. Go to your tasks."

I wiped water from my eyes with my hand to see my way to the kitchen. The storm had passed—the storm which had made me stiff as a stick so that I could not sleep. Now my mind was not able to tell my hands to work; it was turning around and around like leaves still falling to the ground.

Slowly my mind began to arrange itself. I struggled to remember the words of Teacher, easy and few, words with much wisdom. I tried to put his words alongside all the other affairs of life I had known before this day. I wanted to see clearly what this affair of stealing—this affair which had tortured my heart—had taught me.

I understood now that all white men do not have the same heart. Teacher was different from Bula Matadi. He did not show anger of fire. He did not whip us. Truly, I did not understand all the affairs of Teacher. But now I did understand that he loved us. What he had just done proved this to us. Because of this love, Father would never know the shame which almost caught him. We would go home tonight and sit with him at the fire again; we would rejoice together, as all other days. I could not believe it for happiness.

I began to understand other things; these caused me new joy. Teacher mentioned the affair of the Son of Mvidi Mukulu, as Father had told us. Teacher said Mvidi Mukulu did not like killing, lying, stealing. These were laws of Mvidi Mukulu which Father had spoken to us many times. It began to appear that Mvidi Mukulu of the white man and Mvidi Mukulu of our forefathers was the same.

I had wanted to pass up others in the affairs of earth. This desire, which burned my insides, had made me break the laws of Mvidi Mukulu. Thus I had stumbled badly. Stumbling again would leave me behind forever. I could not progress by breaking the laws of Mvidi Mukulu. Did I not know that He was stronger than I? Even the wren remembers who feeds it. To respect the laws of Mvidi Mukulu must be my first affair, progressing in the affairs of earth must follow behind.

Finally, Teacher spoke of forgiveness. This affair made me happiest of all. The Son of Mvidi Mukulu did have a way to whiten hearts, as the moon whitened the ground between our huts. He could chase away evil spirits into the darkness, as I had hoped. He could give my heart joy that would make me want to dance and sing again!

The words of Teacher had been few. I did not yet understand the path of forgiveness. But my heart rejoiced with all its strength to know that there was a forgiveness path, a path in the sunshine for all to see, a path which I could find and follow. I promised myself that I would never get into bad affairs again. I promised myself that when I found the path, I would follow it all the days of my life.

In the days which followed, Mutombo and I refused to see our friend Kabeya. Our affair with him was finished. We ate no more things of the white man. We guarded ourselves well. Then one day a black stranger came. He helped me finish the most important affair in my life. He showed me the path.

His name was Daniel Tshisanga. He had lived for many years with the white man. He had learned many affairs from the Book of Mvidi Mukulu. Speaker had called him to teach us.

Daniel gathered people from everywhere—from the villages—from the medicine hut—children from class. We sat all in one group. He taught us every day for a week. He taught us amazing affairs, affairs which had never yet entered our ears. Being one of us, he spoke our language. I had opened my ears. His teaching lightened up my mind as a torch lightens the inside of a dark hut.

He said that our customs show us clearly that long ago our

forefathers had known the path of Mvidi Mukulu well. Their laws of justice and judgment were good. They talked of the Son of Mvidi Mukulu. They offered blood sacrifices to atone for sin. But some of these affairs had become twisted, and others like them had been lost because they had been guarded only in people's minds.

People of another tribe had kept these affairs in a Book. This Book was among us now. Daniel had come to teach us from it. He had come to tell us again the affairs of Mvidi Mukulu of our forefathers.

He told us of the creation of things in the beginning. He told us how sin had caught the hearts of all men on earth. He told us more affairs of the coming of the Son of Mvidi Mukulu upon earth. He straightened our story of how the Son of Mvidi Mukulu had exceeded the power of death. Above all these things, he told a fable which showed us how the Son of Mvidi Mukulu had bought for us forgiveness.

"There was a village which suffered greatly because of an angry lion," Daniel said. "At night, when all were sleeping like dead people, the lion would come out of the jungle. He would slip up to a hut, suddenly break the door and steal a person. Sometimes he would steal an old person, sometimes he would steal a child, sometimes he would steal a person of strength. When hunger caught him, he would come again. He had great hunger. He came many times. Many people disappeared. No one was safe. No one could restrain him. The villagers were all caught with terrible fear.

"One night the lion stole another villager. When morning came, the chief called the villagers together. He said, 'The hunger of this lion will never be finished. If we do nothing, we shall all die. We must find wisdom to kill this lion while we are still sufficient in number. In many-ness there is strength. Let us together get our bows and arrows. Let us as one man track the lion and kill him.'

62

"The men got their weapons. They followed the lion's tracks a long distance until they came to a little path between two great stones. They stood between the stones and looked for the path. It went down slowly between the bushes along the wall of a ravine. Their eyes followed the path until it led to a clearing. In the clearing stood the lion. He was standing among the bones of people. He was still eating their tribemate. Behind him was the entryway to a cave.

"The lion stopped eating and lifted his head. He smelled the air. He turned and saw the men standing between the rocks. He roared with terrible anger. He turned and leaped, running toward the men. They scattered into the jungle, losing each other. The men returned to the village, each finding his own path, as warriors shamed by defeat.

"The next day the chief called the men together again. 'Now we know where the lion lives,' he said. 'When he comes from the ravine to hunt food, he must come on the path between the big rocks. If a good hunter waited for him, he could kill him. Who accepts to go with his weapon to the big rocks tonight to kill the lion?'

"The men looked at each other. One said guests were coming to his house. Another said it would be foolish to leave his wife and children home alone at night. No one accepted to go wait for the lion.

" 'Is there no one with bravery?' the chief asked. 'Are you all weak as women? Is there no one who will offer himself to save our village?'

"Then a strong man stood. 'I will go,' he said. All the men looked at him. It was the chief's son, his only son.

"The chief did not want his son to go. Yet, his words about bravery bound him. He would not be shamed before his villagers. He accepted for his son to go.

"The son took his weapons and left. People did not sleep

well that night. They awaited the return of the chief's son. He did not return. When day came, people feared to go hunt for him. The second night came. Again, people did not sleep well. They said, 'If the lion killed the son last night, he will come to kill one of us tonight.'

"When three nights had passed, the villagers asked each other, 'Why has the son not returned? Why has the lion not returned?' They were shamed to sit any longer. The men took their weapons and slowly began the journey toward the big rocks on the edge of the ravine.

"They were walking in a long row along the path in the jungle and were coming close to the great rocks when suddenly the men in the front of the line shouted, 'Look! The lion is dead!'

"They ran rapidly to see. They found the carcass of the lion. Under the lion was the body of the chief's son. He had died to save the village."

Daniel explained for us the story.

"Like the lion was killing everybody, so sin was slaying all men. As no one could restrain the lion, so men had no power to conquer sin. All men would die. But when we were sinners, when we had no strength to save ourselves, the great Chief, Mvidi Mukulu, loved us. He had only one Son; His name was Jesus. He accepted for His Son to go fight sin. Jesus fought with sin and conquered it. He broke its power forever. But in the battle He paid with His life. He died. He took the deaths of all of us upon Himself. Because He suffered we have happiness. Because He died we can live without fear of death.

"If we are sorry for our evil ways," Daniel continued, "and turn away from sin, if we open our hearts for Jesus to enter and begin walking in His path, then Mvidi Mukulu will erase all our bad affairs. Then sin cannot destroy us. When our life on earth is finished, we will go to Mvidi Mukulu with no affair. We will sit in His village of happiness forever."

When Daniel spoke these words my heart leaped. It was like the affair of Ndaya. Because of her suffering, we received the joy of coming across the river. Now the suffering and dying of Jesus brought me happiness—the forgiveness of all my sins. I loved the Son of Mvidi Mukulu. I wanted Him, with my whole body. I wept for my sins. I turned away from them. I opened my heart for Jesus to enter. I put my life into His path. I felt cleanness entering inside me. I found peace. Then my heart began singing with the happiness of a tiny bird singing in a great nsanga tree. The words of Tshisanga had forever answered the affairs which had been in my heart from childhood.

Mutombo and many other class children found peace too. We were put into a class where they taught us the customs of those who follow Jesus. When this class finished, we fulfilled one of those customs which followers of Jesus call "baptism." To show that we had begun a new way of life, we took new names for ourselves. I chose the name of David, Mutombo chose the name of John.

Now that I had opened my ears to the affairs of Mvidi Mukulu, my mind was opened to better understand affairs in class. These affairs were like more torches which lightened up other dark places in my mind so that I could see things I had never seen before. Once I had been as a person lost in the darkness of jungle. Now I felt I was standing on a high point of a great prairie. On all sides of me I could look out to the ends of the earth.

I learned about other countries, countries near us, countries far across the great water. I learned about the people of these countries. I learned of the affairs of these countries. I learned that Bula Matadi had come from the country of Belgium and that Speaker and Teacher had come from

America. I learned where the white foreigners had come from who had brought guns to strange tribesmen and enabled them to enslave us. I learned their names—Arabs and Portuguese. I learned why they wanted tribesmen to believe they would someday rule all tribes. These white men had hoped to use them to keep catching slaves forever.

I learned where my stolen tribemates had disappeared to. Those who had not died of suffering along the path were sent across the water beyond where the sun sets. They and their offspring worked without pay so white men could be rich and live at ease. These affairs helped me to understand that, truly, all white men do not have one heart.

I finished the class where they taught us numbers and reading. Then I started studying in the class where they taught only affairs from the Book of Mvidi Mukulu. By this time, parts of the Book had been turned around into our own language. I began reading these parts for myself. I marveled greatly to find in it many laws and customs like our own—the law of revenge of an eye for an eye, the laws of a widow and her children being cared for by the next younger brother of her dead husband, the law of cleansing of the mother after she gives birth to a child.

This was truly the book of our forefathers. I felt much sadness because for so long a time my people had died without knowing about it. But what about the people of today? They were still living; they had not yet heard. They must learn the news of Jesus. This was news that would make all ears want to listen; it would make all hearts happy. I must tell them. I would be a speaker of the affairs of Mvidi Mukulu for all the days of my life. Thus I would bring to many other people the happiness that Daniel Tshisanga had brought to me.

The day I determined to be a speaker for Jesus, I did not want to wait until class was finished. My heart tugged at me

66

to go tell Mother and Father what I was going to do with the days of my life.

When I arrived home Mother was in the kitchen hut at the fire preparing supper. I spoke to her some words from the Book. I told her what I wanted to do. Her face showed me it was good. Her ears were thirsty like the dry season soil.

I did not tell Father when he first arrived home. I waited until after supper when we sat at the fire. I spoke to him words from the Book and told him what my heart desired. He did not look at me but looked at the ground. He listened but his ears were like stones.

I began to understand that my faith in Jesus would bring me trouble. It might divide me from Father. It might also separate me from honored customs of our forefathers. It could kill friendship between my relatives or clansmen and myself. It could invoke upon me the anger of ancestral spirits. I began to understand that because of Jesus great storms could beat upon me. I could expect them from many different directions. They would beat upon me as long as I followed the path of Jesus. I strengthened my heart. I was in the path now. I would not turn back.

One of these storms, which grew slowly for many days, began when I faced the next big affair in my life.

* * *

Night makes all travelers one-eyed; then no one can see the path, nor the end of the journey.

7

Mutombo and I studied the Book. We studied it hard. We ate it as people whose stomachs are too big to be filled. We learned that the One our forefathers had called Mvidi Mukulu was the same Person the white man called God. He was the one great Chief of all the tribes of earth. His Son had been one with Him from the beginning. This Son had two names. While He was walking among people of earth for a few days, His name was Jesus; but while He sat with Mvidi Mukulu, at the home of the rains and dry seasons, His name was Christ.

As baby monkeys fasten themselves to their mother's breasts when they feed or to her body when she runs, so we fastened ourselves to the affairs in the Book. Mutombo began to feel as I did—that it would be great happiness to always be telling other people the good news about Jesus Christ. We wanted to tell our own people; we wanted to tell people of other tribes.

In our spirits, Mutombo and I were as infants hunting breasts to cling to, but in our bodies we were no longer infants. We had begun having the desires of grownup people. We began thinking about the years ahead of us. We knew people in strange villages would not cook meals every day for us. They would not let us live in their homes. Thus we could not go live among them and teach them of Christ without our having helpmates. While we were still studying, it was time to begin looking for those who were to make the happiness of our lives complete. We decided to discuss this affair with Father.

"Your request is good," Father said. "One chain on an arm doesn't talk. And your years are about sufficient for you to find wives. But there is one thing that troubles us—wealth. Where shall we get sufficient wealth for two bride-prices? A poor man's palm nuts yield little oil."

"You have worked hard for Bula Matadi many years," Mutombo said. "Are not your riches sufficient to get us wives?"

"When I was a young man, the wealth I now have would have been sufficient," Father replied. "However, many of the white man's things have come among us. Look at the kinds of things you see in our markets now—cloth, soap, salt, lamp oil, fish locked in cups, writing sticks, paper. Look how much one must pay for seven arms' length of cloth! Men's lust for things has raised the prices they ask for their daughters."

"When will you have sufficient wealth?" I asked.

"If Disanka and Ditekemena were with us, this affair would not trouble us," he said. "By this time, young men would have paid me bride-prices to marry them. As is the custom, these riches would get wives for you. You see how the affair the white man did long ago is still troubling us, clear up to today."

"But Ndaya is still with us," I said.

"Truly. For her they will give me the price of one bride. When I receive a bride-price for her, what shall we do with it? Shall we divide it between the two of you so each of you can marry a useless woman of little value? You won't catch healthy rats if you put your traps in the mud. With poor women, neither of you would be happy. The bride-price I receive for Ndaya will suffice for getting a wife for Mutombo; but you remain."

"What are you saying?" I asked in surprise. "That I will waste the days of my life without a wife? What kind of suffering that would be! Do not the fathers say, Give the elder son his thing, give the younger son his thing—thus your generation will be perpetuated?"

"They also say that the younger born is the unfortunate one—he is the slave. Now you will begin to understand that on that day when the white man did us badly, suffering caught all of us. How shall I answer your question? Let the white man tell you where to find wealth for you to marry."

Father's words saddened me. They showed me that my getting a wife would be difficult. They also showed me that the seeds of hatred against the white man were still alive and strong in Father's heart. They were still alive in the hearts of many fathers. I feared they would remain alive for generations, waiting for a time to spring forth. If that time should arrive they would spring forth and bear fruit of terrible revenge.

Hatred wanted to rise in my own heart—hatred against the white man whose lust had robbed us of wealth. Because of his lust I was now deprived of a helpmate. Then I remembered my Friend Jesus. He had brought me the light and joy of forgiveness. Hatred and revenge were affairs of darkness. I did not belong to darkness any longer. I belonged to Jesus Christ of God. I must stay in His path. If He wanted me to work for Him in a faraway village, He would arrange these affairs. He would give me what I needed for my happiness to be sufficient.

"Let Mvidi Mukulu do as He wishes," I said.

Mutombo spoke his wisdom. "Many young men who have finished class and know numbers well are working for Bula Matadi and other white men," he said. "They are hunting for wives. They do not want pagan village women who know nothing. Their work gives them much wealth. They will pay high bride-prices for women who know some of the white man's wisdom. Ndaya is well-mannered. She has a sufficient bit of intelligence. If she went to class across the river, she would learn something about numbers and get accustomed to some of the ways of the white man. Then a young man of wealth would ask to marry her. He would pay you a high bride-price for her. She would be married by a man of honor and means. When I marry, some of the wealth might be left over to help Mulumba."

"We will ask Ndaya," Father said. "Her bride-price will be used for Mutombo to marry. If wealth remains, good. If we fail sufficient wealth for a wife for Mulumba, we aren't helpless, as animals. A goat scratches its itching flank against a tree, but a man can ask his kinsmen to scratch him. I know where two of my brothers sit. The journey will be long, but we could go ask them to help us with wealth, as is our custom in such an affair."

We had heard that two of Father's brothers had broken their tether ropes of slavery. They had fled down the river to the city of Kinshasa, where the greatest Bula Matadi and his helpers lived. I did not want my uncles to enter the affair of my marriage. I well knew the proverb: Make friends with a pepper and its children will burn you.

It is best that a father have sufficient wealth to pay bride-prices for all his sons. He heeds the words of the elders who say, Pay your child the debt you owe him, else when you are toothless, he'll not feed you. The father secures wives for his sons. Thus there is no trouble. The sons return kindness to their father when he is old and the affair is finished. However, when a father's brothers' wealth is used for a bride-price, they, and even their children, remain part owners of the bride, until they are repaid. Many troubles can follow.

If my uncles helped me with wealth, they would expect

71

my wife to bear children. When my daughters grew up, bride-prices I received for them could not be used to secure wives for my sons. These bride-prices must be used to pay the debt I owed my uncles, whose wealth I'd used and enjoyed these many years. Thus I would not have wealth to help my sons secure wives, and they must go beg wealth from their uncles. Thus the yoke of debt which I first took upon myself would be passed on from generation to generation.

If my wife fails to bear children, our custom gives me one path by which to finish my indebtedness to my uncles. I must marry another woman who will bear girl children. What would I do with my first wife? A barren woman is as worthless as a dead stick. I could send her back to her parents and they would refund to me my bride-price. Because she could not bear, she would probably get money for her food and clothing by selling her body to any man who passes in the path.

I would use the bride-price refunded me to purchase another wife. The girl children she bears me would grow up and enter marriages; bride-prices I received for them would be used to repay my uncles. However, if I should keep my barren wife, my second wife must bear girl children sufficient to pay off the bride-prices of both my wives.

Parents give a daughter to a man for marriage only if they receive a bride-price. It closes the marriage covenant. It binds the wife to her husband. Women who live with men without the paying of bride-prices are harlots.

Thus Mutombo hunted wisdom to help me find wealth for a bride-price. Ndaya went across the river. She studied there for a year. She was married by a young man of sufficient wealth named Leta. She went with him far away to the large village of Lubumbashi. He would work for the white men who mined and sold red iron which was found there.

Leta was one of many of our tribemates who finished numbers and reading classes across the river and went to faraway villages to work for other white men. Some of our young clansmen went to Makala to help white men who were digging hard stones called diamonds from the streams. Others went down the river to Kinshasa, to work for the white people of the great Bula Matadi who lived there. Thus our tribemates were scattered across our country as strong seed hunting soil in which to grow.

More and more children of our tribemates came from many different places to enter class. Many of their parents were still slaves, as my parents had been. Our former masters did not follow after the children. They did not want Bula Matadi to discover their secret tribal customs. Thus, they sat in their secluded villages and tried to keep those of Father's generation as their slaves. Because their old ways brought them happiness, they did not send many of their children to school.

Thus the seeds began to grow, and bit by bit, our tribe began to exceed the tribe of our masters in wisdom and authority.

The girls who came to class were few. It was not our custom that men and women be the same. As vegetable leaves, women are stupid, the elders said. We abuse them, and they still feed us. A father knows that a boy baby will keep his name alive upon earth for a generation. A girl baby means only things. When she grows up, she will be bartered for pigs and goats and cloth. The wealth these things bring will be used to secure wives for his sons. From these marriages will come his grandsons, who will thus keep his name alive for another generation.

Men are strong and brave. They hunt animals and go to

battle. Women are weak. They sit at home and do little useless things like splitting firewood, drawing water from the stream, cooking in smoke filled kitchens and raising children. For this reason, of man's two hands, the one he works with is called "the man's hand"; the weaker, helping hand is called "the woman's hand." Our forefathers believed Mvidi Mukulu willed it this way. Had not the woman disobeyed Him in the beginning and brought all troubles upon man?

Speaker and Teacher did not agree with these customs. They said they wanted to heal the sores in our minds as well as the sores on our bodies. They said one bad sore was our custom by which men made women their slaves. Where the sore is, that's where the medicine cloth goes. Speaker and Teacher built a sleeping-house for girls. By giving gifts, they lured girls away from their homes to come live with them at the mission post. They taught these girls all the knowledge they taught boys. More than this, wives of the white men also taught girls the affairs of women. These girls were few. They started class when they were older. Their years were almost sufficient for them to enter marriage.

Doing these things did not please the elders of our tribe. They did not know what this would do to us and our people in the days to come. Women do not have the same intelligence as men, they said. If women learned as much as men, they would become insolent and rebellious. It was wrong for women to be taught affairs that would make them forget their tasks of bearing children and working at their homes.

While Ndaya was in class, Mutombo met a girl of our tribe named Mbuyi. She was one of the few girls who lived away from home on the mission post. After Ndaya married, Father went to Mbuyi's parents and arranged the brideprice. Mutombo and Mubyi were married by Speaker in the house where we met to worship God. They built their home of sticks and mud on the edge of the jungle clearing behind the mission post in the shade of great nsanga trees which stood behind them like a row of straight tall soldiers keeping the jungle from swallowing them.

One day Speaker said in class, "This is the second year that you young men are studying the affairs of God and His Book. There remains one year for you to finish. When you go to live in villages far away, you will not only teach people about God and His Son, you will also teach their children to read and write. As you have learned, you must help others to learn. Your teaching will be as knives which cut cords of ignorance that bind men's minds.

"It is not good for you to begin to teach only when you arrive in the village of strangers," he said, "You must sharpen your teaching knives well. Then when you arrive among strange villagers, when they see your wisdom for working with their children, they will respect you. They will care for you well.

"The number of children coming to learn passes up our strength to teach them," Speaker continued. "You young men will help us. We will divide them into groups. We will give each of you a group of children to teach. You will begin to teach them to read and write."

We were to teach our children during the hours of morning; we were to study the affairs of Jesus in class in the hours of afternoon. We were to begin teaching the first school day of next week, which we had learned to call Monday.

Teacher encouraged me. He said I had worked well in his house. If my stealing had wounded him, he covered the scar so I could not see it. He said I had learned many things that other class children did not know. He said it was not good for work in his house to interfere with my more important work of teaching. He would find a young class child to help him in the house. I should now give myself to teaching other small children the many things I had learned all of these days in his classes and in his house.

I was happy. I was no longer a child. I was about to arrive at the stature of a man. I was as one who had been given his first hoe and was sent to make his own field. If you lie to your neighbors about the work you're doing in your field, your house will soon reveal it, the elders say. I would not be accused of having a lazy hoe. I would grip my work with two hands. I would do it well.

Teacher said I had learned many things other children my age had not learned because I had worked these years in his house. Speaker knew this also. Thus I hoped they would honor me by giving me one of the best groups of children. They would want me to use well the things I had learned.

I did not want to wait until Monday. My heart trembled, like the heart of a bird being pushed from its nest to fly. My mind would not stick to my work of studying. It always wanted to show me a picture—rows of children expectant and fearful as I had been seven years ago, rows of hungry little blackbirds waiting to be fed.

Monday arrived. We stood before Speaker to be sent to classes we were to teach. When Speaker came to me he said, "Mulumba, you will teach the group that has gathered in the house of God. You will teach them there until we are able to build a class hut for them."

I approached the house of God, my heart trembling. I arrived at the door, stopped and swallowed to quiet my insides. I entered. I looked at my class of children. They were girls—all girls—the girls who lived on the mission post!

I threw my back to their faces, left the house and cut a straight path to talk to Speaker.

"That class is not sufficient for me to teach," I told him.

"Why not?"

"You have watched me and my work these many years. I have studied hard. Also I worked alongside the white man in his house. To do this work, every morning I came across the river while all my classmates were yet sleeping. I stayed until after they had all gone home at night. Now you count me as being worth less than any of my classmates. You give them all classes of boys to teach; you give me this handful of girl children."

"It is not thus," he replied. "Will a champion become stronger by breaking twigs, or by felling trees? When Teacher and I thought of the class of girls, we hunted a champion. We asked ourselves, 'Who has the most patience? Who has most given himself to work for Jesus? Who will exceed all others in trying?' While we know that others are able to break twigs, we felt that you are able to fell this tree. When you do, you will be the greater champion. The greater trees you find in years ahead will not make you fear."

Speaker did not know my classmates would snicker at me. He did not know my parents would offend me. But to refuse his words would be like telling him I was not a champion. I decided I would try. I knew that Mutombo would strengthen me. We both had large strong bodies for our age. When someone offended me, we could bring his words to an end quickly. And Mutombo would help keep my parents from knowing.

We did not need to take care of ourselves. If anyone spoke words of ridicule, we did not hear them. After some days had passed, I began to see that God had arranged things this way. He had wanted me to teach the class of girl children. He was teaching me too.

I discovered that girl children learn as rapidly as boy children. The one who exceeded them all in sharpness of wisdom was Ngalula. The faces of the others were more beautiful, but her bright eyes showed me her heart. Her eyes were not afraid. They were honest and trusting. Her mind was hungry to learn things.

I began to watch her closely. Always she was with the first girls arriving in the morning. Her smooth, well-formed body was always freshly bathed. She carried herself well. She was more quiet-mannered; she did not join other girls in their noisy jabbering and senseless giggling.

I was a teacher. I could not be with her more than I was with any other of my students. But when they all played outside between classes, I found that I was watching Ngalula. When class was finished and the children left for home my eyes followed Ngalula until she disappeared. Then the picture would remain in my mind. It would not let me study well in the afternoons. It made me happy as I lay awake at night.

I wanted to learn more about Ngalula. I began to feel that if she were to be my helpmate, I would be surpassingly happy. However, I could not speak to her of these things. I would learn about her some other way.

There was the teacher-chief who kept a book with all the names and affairs of the class children written in it. I told him that I needed to learn some things about the children in my class. He took me into his workroom and let me look into the book. While he watched me, I began writing names of parents of my class children; the first, the second, the third. When he turned away to do other work, I quickly followed down the row to the name of Ngalula. I saw that she was of my tribe. Her father was Tambwe; her mother was Odia. They lived at the village of Kanyinga. It was the village on the hill above Luaba! I wrote these things quickly, closed the book, and went to the door.

"Have you already finished?" the teacher-chief asked.

"Yes, thank you," I said and left rapidly.

The affairs of class did not find much room in my mind that afternoon. When class ended I ran home and waited for Father. He arrived and sat down to wait while Mother prepared supper. I spoke.

"Father, Mutombo is married and is happy. I want to arrange the affair of a wife."

"Yes."

"I have seen a young girl across the river who makes me happy. Her parents live in the village of Kanyinga. Would you go discuss the affair of bride-price with them?"

"Does she want you?"

"Yes," I said. I did not know this was true, but I told myself inside that she had not refused me.

"What are the names of her parents?"

"Tambwe and Odia."

"On the seventh day I have no work. I will go talk with them."

On the evening of the seventh day I was waiting for him at the house when he returned.

"Did you speak with them?"

"Yes."

"Has someone else asked to marry her?"

"No."

"What bride-price do they ask?"

"Five goats, a pig, eight pieces of new cloth and twelve iron hoe heads. It is a hard price."

"Is this the end price, or are they still bargaining?"

"Perhaps they will still bargain. But where will we find this many things? It would be better for you to find a girl of a lower price. As the proverb goes, Be content to eat a chicken's wing; rejecting it, you may get its head."

"What kind of woman has a low price? One with an empty head, or who is stubborn as a goat, or who doesn't have clean body habits, or a talebearer who gathers people's heads to carry around her neck. Such a woman would not make me happy. She would bring shame upon you and Mother too. Why wash my hands with saliva when I could bathe in a river? Must we be stingy about wealth when we are choosing one thing that will make us happy all the days of our life?"

"A good man tied to a bad woman is like a hunting dog tied to a jackal. It is good to have one who makes you happy. Only a small part of Ndaya's bride-price remains. I do not have sufficient wealth. When your studying work is finished, we will arrange a trip to go see your uncles."

I did not answer at once. I was afraid. If I went to my uncles, I would put a yoke of debt on my neck. What if affairs of the future made this yoke too heavy for me to carry? What if Ngalula bore me no children?

No man rejoiced when his wife could not bear. But there always had been a way of escape. He would return the woman to her parents, receive back the bride-price, and with it marry another woman. What happened to his first wife did not trouble him—he had given her many days to fulfill her duty and she had failed. She was of no value.

What we learned in the Book of God changed these affairs. If Ngalula did not bear children, I could not drive her from my home for her to live as a harlot. Speaker taught us that people working for Jesus could have only one wife. Thus I could not marry a second wife who would bear and thereby repay my uncles. Now the way of escape was closed. If Ngalula did not bear I would be trapped as a rooster in a carrying-basket. Even if I turned around and around hunting, even if I pecked and pecked forever, I would not escape.

People who work for God do not get much money. I could not hope to pay my debt this way. If Ngalula bore no children, I would die in shame, disgraced by my relatives, because my uncles had never been paid.

Perhaps I should not marry Ngalula. Then what woman should I marry? Was Ngalula worse than any other woman? In some tribes, men would cause their women to have baby-stomachs, and then would marry them; thus there was no danger of troubles caused by barren marriages. But I could not do thus.

There was one way to escape these dangers: to not marry. But among us, a single person is the same as a dead person; he never reproduces.

An animal does not live in its den for fear of being caught in a trap. It must graze. There was no other way for me. I would marry Ngalula, a woman of high price, drink my cup full of happiness and carry great debt. Maybe these problems would catch us. Maybe they would not. If they did I would carry the debt all my days and die in shame. Or I would quit the work of God, marry another woman who would bear me children and leave the judgment of my affair in the hands of God who understands our burdens on earth. Or He might have other wisdom with which to arrange the affair. I wanted happiness. I belonged to God. If there were burdens in the path ahead of me, He would help me carry them.

"Yes," I said to Father. "Let us go see my uncles."

* * *

A hole dug too deep will swallow the digger.

8

The year of school ended. I spoke to Ngalula. She accepted with happiness. Father and I secured much of the bride-price from my uncles, Tshibuabua and Kabambi, at the city of Kinshasa. The marriage contract was closed. Speaker married us in the house of Mvidi Mukulu. He prayed that we be happy with each other and that our home be blessed with children.

I said in my heart, "So let it be."

Ngalula and I were very happy. How had I gotten such a woman? As the elders say, Not by birthright, not by good looks, but by luck. I answered with a different proverb: Good things don't come by themselves; God gives them to people.

Mutombo helped me build a hut of mud and sticks alongside his. During the hours we worked together, we opened our hearts to each other. We talked of the joy we would have teaching the good news of Jesus Christ in strange villages.

Mutombo spoke to me of another affair which I refused to tell Ngalula. He and Mbuyi had been living together for more than a year. Mbuyi had not yet conceived. He was being taunted and offended by other young men whose wives were bearing children.

"This trouble should not overwhelm you," I said. "There is no debt. You owe no one anything for Mbuyi."

"You know our clansmen say, Women are married to bear children; if it were for their prettiness, we would have neglected them. Moreover, we owe Father a debt of honor.

He will not live forever. He must see that we have done our part to remove him one generation from memories of shame."

We finished our last year of class. Mutombo was to go to the far north village of Lusama; I was to go to the village of headhunters called Kele. When we left each other, Mutombo was not with the happiness we had talked about having.

"Failing to bear children is a bad snare," he said. "My friends ask why I waste the years of my strength with a woman who is barren. We all know that to bear is trouble, but to be barren is worse. Father has begged me to send Mbuyi to her parents and to use his bride-price money for another woman who will give offspring. This I do not want to do. But the burden of shame is hard to carry."

"Strengthen your heart," I said. "Maybe the happiness of working for Jesus will overcome the sadness of this burden. Maybe in the village of strangers, He will answer your prayers."

"Strangers are not better than people we know," he said. "It will be a big stumbling stone if they see I am not as other men. I don't want to fail in the work of Jesus. If He does not help me in this affair, I fear I will stumble."

Thus we left each other to begin our work—the work of "sowers," or in the white man's tongue, of "evangelists." Mutombo went with a heart of burden; I went with a heart of joy. We did not know when we would see each other again.

I had arrived at a big day in my life. The affairs of childhood were behind me. The affairs of studying were finished. Now I was turning my back on my parents, my classmates and my teachers. I stood as a man, alone.

The path ahead of me led into jungle where few people had cut paths—a jungle so thick light never chases away the evil spirits; the spirits live there, disturbed by nothing.

As I became acquainted with the ways of the headhunting people, I began to understand the greatness of the trees in that jungle. Even if I were a champion, I would need all of my strength to fell them.

These people lived four days' foot journey to the west of Luaba. Some of their villages were holes cleaned out of the middle of the jungle; others were near streams on the rolling prairie. All their villages were away from paths traveled by strangers. They did not want foreigners to upset their customs. They wanted to be alone.

Bula Matadi would not leave them alone. He traveled among them from time to time. He wanted to know the number of their people. He wanted to make them pay taxes. Thus they would acknowledge him as their chief and could be ruled by his laws. They could be made to stop hunting the heads of others.

Bula Matadi was strong because his soldiers carried guns. But he also greatly respected the work of Speaker and Teacher. When he went into a new village of the headhunters, he would ask Speaker to send an evangelist with him. The evangelist would help him explain why he had come to visit the village. Thus the villagers would not revolt against him. He could gain authority over them without using the guns of his soldiers.

One day Speaker called me and said, "Bula Matadi is planning a trip into the headhunters' villages next week. This is a good time for you to go with him and begin working at your village."

"May I take Ngalula with me?"

"Our evangelists have entered some other headhunter villages. But none has ever entered the village of Kele. It is good to measure the water before you throw yourself into it. We do not know what the people will say about your coming to teach them. Perhaps they will refuse you; perhaps they will accept you. If you are able to stay, will the villagers sit with you peaceably? We cannot know now. It is not good for Ngalula to go with you at this time. When you see the people are friendly and you have built your own house, then you may come get Ngalula."

I told Ngalula the plans.

"How long will you be gone?" she asked.

"I do not know."

"What if the village people do you evil? Then I will be left alone. If something happens, it would be better that we disappear from earth together."

"No evil will catch me. I will guard myself well. Did not Jesus promise to be with us to the end of the earth? I will return."

"Do not stay away too long," she said. "You know that when one sits many days alone, the body joins the heart in loneliness and destroys one's good wisdom. Thus temptations ensnare us."

"I will ask Teacher to let you help with the class children. He and Helper will strengthen your heart."

Bula Matadi, twelve soldiers and I began the journey the third day, called Wednesday. I wrapped my things into a blanket bundle. The soldiers carried their bundles and guns. When we slept at night, soldiers stayed awake to guard us. Because we stopped at other villages along the path, we arrived at the footpath to Kele on the seventh day.

We left the big path and followed the footpath into the grass on our right hands. When we reached the top of a hill we saw the village. About twenty huts sat in a circle in a cleared-off place on the low prairie before us. The soldiers with their guns and red caps went ahead in the line. Bula Matadi and I followed behind.

"Have you visited this village before?" I asked him.

"No. I have visited other villages in this area. These people have heard about me."

"Are they expecting your arrival?"

"I think they are expecting us. We cannot know if they expect to welcome us or if they expect to refuse us. It is for this that you may help us."

"What will we do if they refuse us?"

"That is why I bring soldiers with guns."

As we came near, we saw that the houses were made of palm leaves tied in place by strips of bamboo. Each house was hooked to the next one by a tight bamboo fence. All house doors faced into the circle. Thus the houses and fences made a circle wall without a hole for entering. The closed-in village always turned its back on us, like a woman who always wanted to hide what her hands were doing.

A door in the wall fence opened. From it came a tall slender man wearing a loincloth and carrying a spear. After him came another with a bow and arrow. After him was another—a line of them came. They stopped and stood in a row facing us. An older man, with bald head, stooped shoulders and gray beard, stepped ahead of the line and stood proudly, waiting to meet us.

Bula Matadi touched my arm.

"Go speak to him," he said.

I stepped ahead of the soldiers. I was being watched by the village men as a monkey about to steal corn from their fields. I stretched out my hand and said, "We have not come to trouble you. We have come to talk with you. Would you show us places to sit down?"

He did not shake my hand. Maybe he did not understand this white man's sign of friendship. He grunted and walked toward a roof sitting on four crooked sticks to one side of the cleaned space. His men followed him. On the ground beneath the roof was a great village anvil stone on which they made their weapons. Beside it were ashes where there had been a forging fire.

With his hand he showed us places to sit down on pieces of logs and stones here and there in the shade of the roof. He sat on the edge of his chair, looking, waiting, as a surprised animal not knowing what to do to escape being caught. His men squatted around him, holding their weapons.

"I am the chief," he said. "Speak your affair."

Bula Matadi spoke through his helper who turned around his words. He told them why he had come into their country. I had heard these words before. Father had told them to me. Father had heard Bula Matadi speak them many years before when he and many others were brought from their villages to Luaba and sat on the hillside in front of Bula Matadi's house where it faced the river.

He finished speaking and waited for their reply. The chief did not speak. He did not look at his men. He did not move. He looked straight at Bula Matadi. None of them moved. They all sat quiet and proud. When time passed, the chief said, "Are your affairs finished?"

"We have brought this young man," Bula Matadi said, pointing his finger to me. "I will leave him in your village to teach your children to write numbers and to read from paper leaves. He is the owner of a good heart. He will do you no evil. When I return with my soldiers another time, I want to find him with strength. You will guard him well. Do you understand?"

There was only silence, and the proud hard look.

"Have you no word to speak?" Bula Matadi asked.

After more silent time passed, the chief spoke. "If the young man does not enter into our tribal affairs, he will have no trouble."

"Good. I have no other words. We go. Stay well."

Bula Matadi and his men rose to leave. I turned my back to the village men and went to speak to him.

"Do you feel that the villagers want me?"

"We have the word of the chief that you will have no trouble," Bula Matadi said.

"When will you return?"

"I do not know. But you need not fear. The chief knows what the soldiers would do to his village if he harmed you. Stay well."

We shook hands of farewell. I watched Bula Matadi and the soldiers walk up the path. I began to feel very alone. I asked Jesus to come stand beside me.

When I turned again to the village men, they were still sitting, looking at me, as masters not understanding what to do with a strange dog which had suddenly appeared among them.

"Sit down," the chief said. "We will enter the village and discuss this affair."

I sat down and watched the men go one by one through the fence gate and disappear inside the village walls. I sat for a time. The sun, lowering in the sky, shined on me. I changed my sitting place to a stone which was in the shade of the roof. I sat a long time. The shadows were growing very long. I began thinking that the strange dog would not be shown to a house. It would not be given a bone to eat. Finally the gate opened. The men returned and took their sitting places. They had no weapons. The chief spoke.

"This is Guama," he said, pointing to a younger man sitting on his heels nearby. "We have chosen him to look after your affairs. He will show you a place to sleep. During the day he will bring you something to eat. A place for you to build your hut is near that tree. We have no other words."

They arose to leave.

I looked at the tree. It was a small tree outside the village circle on the edge of the cleared space. Then I looked at Guama, still sitting nearby. He appeared a bit older than I and a bit more slender. But his arms and shoulders showed much strength.

"I am happy to be here," I said. I feared I was lying.

"I will show you a place to sleep," he said.

He led me to a small hut on the opposite side of the village circle. We went inside it.

"You may sleep here until you finish building your hut," he said. "I will send a child with water. When the sun goes down and the women cook, I will bring you food."

Guama lowered his head, passed through the low door and left. I looked around me. Along the ground, light came in where termites had eaten off the bottom edge of the palm leaf wall. On the floor the dust was deep. There were big holes in the ground where animals had been sleeping. Along one wall, the length of a person, there was a bed frame made of bamboo sticks. It was covered with a mat made of woven swamp reed.

I laid my bundle on the bed. I opened it. I counted the things I had brought—a large jungle knife, a hoe, a small cooking pot, a tin plate and cup, a small cutting knife, a spoon, a small oil lantern, two pairs of trousers, two shirts, a blanket, part of the Book of God called in the white man's tongue a New Testament, a songbook, a notebook of things I had learned in class, a new notebook for writing day to day affairs and two pencils. These were my living things and working things, to help me sit in this village of strangers.

Two boy children came. One, wearing a cord around his waist, carried a gourd with water. The other, wearing nothing, carried a small stool. The first one sprinkled water on the floor of the hut, so that dust lice and jiggers would not trouble me. Then he placed the gourd with water that remained on the floor in the corner. The other placed the stool on the wet floor. They turned to leave.

"What are your names?" I asked.

They stopped, looked at the ground, but did not speak.

"Tell me your names," I said. "I am your friend."

"Loshi," said one, still looking at the ground.

"Yulu," said the other.

"Stay a little and talk with me," I said.

They paused a little. One, still looking at the ground, shook his head. Then he fled. The other one ran after him.

When darkness came, Guama brought me food. At first he did not want to talk, but bit by bit he opened the door of his heart and I began to see friendship. Before he left, he agreed to go with me into the forest tomorrow to show me where to cut sticks to build my own hut.

"I want to come to know the hearts of your people," I said. "I notice that the chief does not want my house to be in the village circle."

"It would not be good for you to live in the village circle," he said.

"Why not?"

He said nothing.

"Guama, I do not want to do one tiny bad thing. I have come to teach you and your people affairs which have given me much joy. If no one tells me the customs of your tribe, I could by accident do something which would cause your people great anger. I could break one of their customs. Then what would they do to me? All affairs would be ruined. Bula Matadi would come and cause you and your people much trouble."

After thinking, Guama said, "It is good for you to know. If you built in the circle of houses, you would pollute our village."

"How would I pollute your village?"

90

"The spirits of our ancestors are not happy for foreigners to walk inside the circle fence of our village."

"Are there other affairs which may pollute your village?"

"Yes."

"What are they?"

"We respect the sacredness of our tree of life."

"Tree of life?" I asked with surprise. "Where is this tree?"

"It is in the center of the village circle. It is the tree of our tribe. It has power to guard us and give us good affairs."

"What kind of good affairs?"

"It gives us feet of good luck when we hunt. It reduces the suffering of our wives when they bear children. It restrains sickness and death."

"Has the tree always been there?"

"No. It was planted."

"How does it get its strength to do all these things?"

"From what is planted beneath it."

"What is planted beneath it?"

"A skull."

"A skull? What kind of a skull?"

"The skull of a person."

"Do you take the skull of someone who dies among you?"

"No. We never use the skull of a tribemate. We cannot use the skull of someone who has already died. Such a skull has lost its power. We take the skull of one who is living."

"How do you get such a skull?"

"We take the skull of a stranger who happens to be among us."

My heart stopped beating until I was sure my ears had not lied to me.

"Does the tree retain its strength forever?" I asked.

"No. When we see bad luck catching our village, we understand that the tree has lost its strength."

"Then what do you do?"

"We leave this place and choose another. We find another tree. We find another skull. We plant them in the new place and build our huts around them. Then our affairs go well again."

I did not want to learn more of their customs this night. I talked of other things until Guama went home. Then I lay on my bed to sleep. But sleep would not catch me. This was a night when the moon had forsaken us. It would come up only when the cock crowed. This night was black as charcoal.

Darkness closed the holes eaten by the termites at the bottom of the wall. It wrapped itself around me tightly like a blanket. I wondered if my ancestral spirits missed me at home. They would never find me here. I wanted to fear, like a fish discarded on the sand, drying in the hot sun, still trying to breathe. My heart began telling me things, things I must remember if I were to stay alive.

I must not violate these people's customs. If I did, they would accuse me of polluting the village. If they decided to move the village elsewhere, finding the skull of a stranger would be no hard affair. A stranger lived among them. If I should try to flee, the only path took me past many other villages of this tribe. There they also might be wanting the skull of a stranger.

I remembered Ngalula's words: "What if the village people do you evil? Then I will be left alone."

I remembered my reply—words which then were very brave: "No evil will catch me. I will guard myself well. Did not Jesus promise to be with us to the end of the earth? I will return."

I was not brave now. I was standing on a rock with much slipperiness in the middle of a river full of crocodiles.

I held my New Testament tightly in my hand. I kneeled beside my bed. I talked these affairs over with Jesus. Then I sang the words of a song we had sung many times when we had felt happy and strong in class:

> Do not fear when trouble comes;
> God will care for you.
> His love is with you.
> God will care for you.
>
> If the tempter comes to you,
> God will care for you.
> Flee to your God.
> He will care for you.

✿ ✿ ✿

When you move to a village of strangers, don't start hunting until you know where they have set their traps.

9

Friendship between the people and me grew very slowly.
The friendship of Guama was of law, not of love. His
outsides, which I saw, belonged to me; but his insides
belonged to others. The chief and elders of the village had
given him an affair to do; he was doing it. His was the only
friendship I had. If I guarded it well, perhaps it would lead
me to friendship with others.

Guama took me to the jungle and showed me where I
could cut sticks for my hut. More than this, he took his knife
and helped me cut them. We cut and carried sticks for three
days. On the morning of the fourth day he brought children
with him: Loshi, Yulu and three others.

"They sit uselessly in the village," Guama said. "They will
help us."

In the days that followed, we cut wall sticks and bamboo
and palm leaves and vines for tying. I saw the children were
happy. A new affair had come to their village. Each day one
or two new ones came. Soon there were twelve. When ten
days had passed, we had finished building my hut under the
tree. While we were looking at my new hut, I spoke to the
children.

"You have done me well," I said. "You have made me a
place to live. As you have helped me and made me happy, I
want to help you and make you happy. Tomorrow morning,
I beg that you come again. You will not work. You will sit
here and I will teach you things your ears have never
heard."

94

The children did not show great joy. A few seemed to show fear. After they were gone, I asked Guama if he would come and sit with us so the children would not fear.

"I will have other work to do," he replied.

"May I get pieces of logs at the place of the roof on crooked sticks? The children will sit on them."

"Those seats are for the work of the chief and elders; it is good for you to make seats for your own work."

In the morning seven children came. I sat on my stool. They sat on the ground.

"I am very happy to see you," I said. "I have many things to show you. These affairs have given me much joy. I will teach you how to make number marks so that you can count well. I will teach you how to make paper leaves talk. I will help you understand the affairs which are passing among other tribes and in other lands. There are too many affairs for you to learn in one day. But remember that slowness does more work than great strength; doing little by little, the work will be finished. We will learn a little every day.

"This first day, I want to speak to you of the affair which is greater than all others; it is the affair of the Son of Mvidi Mukulu. Perhaps your forefathers spoke of Him. He died long ago, but came back to life. Before He died, He promised us who love Him many things. He promised to come and be with us whenever we ask Him to. He promised to do anything we ask Him to do in His name. Our first lesson today is to lower our heads and close our eyes and talk to Him. We will ask Him to come be with us. We will ask Him to help us in our work of studying."

I asked them to bow their heads and close their eyes. When I began to pray, I heard a scuffling of feet. However, I would not open my eyes while praying. I must show them that I was really talking with Jesus from my heart. When I finished praying, I opened my eyes. No one was there. The children had fled.

Then I remembered my first day in class. I remembered how I had peeked with fear between my fingers when Speaker first asked us to close our eyes and pray. These children were more fearful than I had been. They heard me say I was going to speak to One who had died long ago. They would not close their eyes while I talked to the spirit of one long dead. They feared to stay while I talked with a ghost. I had used the wrong words. I had broken their trust in me. Words I had spoken had made them afraid and had chased them away.

The children did not return the next day, nor the next. I passed the time sitting at my hut. Finally on the third day I asked Guama, when he brought me food.

"How can I gather the children to me?"

"Why do you teach them about ghosts?" he replied. "Do you not know they fear ghosts exceedingly? Is not talking with departed spirits of our ancestors the affair of our tribal medicine men? Is it the affair of a stranger who sits among us?"

Two days later something happened which threatened to pollute their village. A woman gave birth to twins. The villagers believed that one woman and one man can produce only one baby; the second could only come by adultery. The villagers were excited. They must rapidly finish rites for cleansing their village or greater curses would follow.

All things the village people possessed which had been made by foreigners were considered unclean. These things, such as cooking pots, or cloth or foreign-made metal things were cast out of the village. The gates were tied shut. Men went into the jungle to hunt and did not return until they had killed nine animals for each of the babies. These animals were taken inside the locked gates. No one would

96

tell me what was done with the animals. One of the babies was painted with whitewash to show that it was unclean. It was not fed and cared for, as the other one. After some days, it died, as they willed.

During this time, once each day Guama brought me food. He carried it on green leaves. When I finished eating, the leaves were discarded. He would not use pots, lest when he returned with them, he carry defilement back into the village.

The twin-baby rituals were finished and the gates were reopened. But there were still signs that things were not well. The chief and his elders spent much time sitting beneath the roof on crooked sticks. They spoke in lowered voices. I could not understand what they were saying, but the movement of their hands and heads showed me they were angry.

Late one afternoon when they were seated talking, Guama came and said, "They are calling you."

I felt as if I'd been hit by an arrow. I arose and went, my insides turning over and over because of fear and many questions. When I arrived, they pointed at a stone. I sat down. The chief spoke.

"These past days many troubles have caught our village," he said. "Can you explain for us where they are coming from?"

"What kind of troubles have caught your village?" I asked.

"Smaller troubles began to appear; they became greater. Then a woman gave birth to twins. We cleansed the village but troubles continue. Now the wife of Putu, an elder, is very ill."

"Troubles catch all people upon earth," I said. "Only Mvidi Mukulu knows why they catch us."

"We do not believe that these troubles have caught us

uselessly. We have a proverb which says, The long sitter is a spy. We believe you know something about these troubles."

"How could I know about them? I have not yet once entered into your village."

There was a time of silence. Then an elder spoke.

"The children have told us that you talk to strange spirits. If you know nothing about these troubles, why did they begin to catch us just after you arrived?"

All eyes looked at me. They burned with anger. I felt my feet slipping off the rock. I was afraid.

"I talk with the Son of Mvidi Mukulu. I talk with Him every day. Have your forefathers not spoken of Him?"

"Why do you speak with Him?" another elder asked.

"Because He has promised to help those who love Him. He has promised to give us what we ask of Him."

"Does He give you the things you ask for?" inquired the chief.

"He has done so many times."

"You are not talking with other spirits which are strange to us?"

"No."

After a pause the chief said, "Go to your hut. We will talk this over. We will call you."

I returned to my hut. I saw that unless I guarded myself well, I would fall into this river of crocodiles. I began praying. In a short time they called me.

"You say that you are innocent of causing us these troubles?" the chief asked.

"Yes."

"You say the Son of Mvidi Mukulu has promised to do for you whatever you ask of Him?"

"Yes."

"Then we will bring the bed with the wife of Elder Putu to your hut. You will ask the Son of Mvidi Mukulu to heal her. If she recovers, then we will know that you are not troubling us and that your words are true."

With these words, the chief had tied me as a prisoner. Would God answer my prayers? He must. If not, how could I escape with my life?

Four men carried the woman to my hut. They placed the bamboo bed beneath the tree outside my door. The woman was very old. Her body was wasted. She was very ill. Guama and Putu stayed. The handle of a knife stuck out from beneath Putu's loincloth. It was getting dark. Guama started a fire. Then they squatted as if they were expecting to stay a long time. They were looking at me.

I placed my stool beside the woman and sat down. I bowed my head and prayed in my heart. I looked at the woman. Nothing had happened.

I got my songbook and sang my songs. Then I prayed again. Nothing happened. The men kept watching me.

Then I kneeled by my stool and cried out to God aloud. I begged Him to heal the woman. I prayed with all the words I knew. I prayed until my insides were dry and hot as an empty pot on a cooking fire. Then I opened my eyes and looked at the woman.

"She is still the same," Putu said.

"Allow me to rest awhile," I begged. "Then I will receive strength to pray some more."

"You are tricking us," Putu said. "Your praying is useless."

"Let us not trouble him yet," Guama said. "He will not run away. Let him rest. Perhaps the spirit he talks with hears better in the light of day."

I lay down on my bed. I did not sleep. I prayed to save my life. Would I escape? Sometimes water eats the best swimmers. I was not afraid to die. I did not think my journey on earth was yet finished. I wanted to see Ngalula again. As I lay, my mind was flooded over with thoughts of her, like the stones of river rapids are covered with rushing water that will not be restrained. When I feared I would never see her again, I wept. When I could push these thoughts from my mind for short pieces of time, I prayed.

Then I thought of other troubles and my heart was further weakened. For many days Ngalula had sat alone. Was she with child when we had left each other? If not, had other married women offended her because she sat uselessly, wasting her days waiting for a husband who perhaps would never return? Other men were always nearby. Had any of them offered to purchase her love?

Mutombo and Mbuyi had not suffered from being separated. They had gone to work for Jesus together. But they had troubles too. Had Mutombo stumbled because of the problem of barrenness? Was he still in the work of Jesus?

But why was I troubling myself with the problems of Mutombo? I had problems too, great problems. An ant sitting on a sieve sees holes everywhere. And so I saw problems encircling me on every side. I was captured. I might soon die. I could do nothing to help Ngalula, or Mutombo, or myself. Why did Jesus let those who work for Him have so many troubles? Why didn't He answer my prayers?

Great trouble does not restrain the coming of a new day. When it was light I rose and went outside. Guama and Putu were still sitting there. The woman looked the same. I sat on the stool.

"Guama," I said. "The Book of Mvidi Mukulu tells us that holy men of long ago would often pray alongside rivers. Thus they would separate themselves from defilement of the affairs of men. They could better talk with Mvidi Mukulu. Accept for me to go to the river to pray."

If they accepted for me to go alone, I could flee. With the help of God I might escape the tribesmen of other villages and reach home. If Guama alone went with me, I might persuade him to save my life by letting me escape.

"He is procrastinating," Putu said. "He can do nothing for the sick one."

"Don't you know spirits will not answer one who is in the midst of uncleanness?" Guama said. "You watch him. I will go discuss this affair with the chief."

Guama returned with a strong-bodied man who carried a spear. Guama had slipped a knife under his loincloth. He spoke to Putu.

"The chief says Guapitshi and I are to tie his hands behind his back and take him to the river. You will stay with the sick one."

I felt weakness of body—weakness that made my stomach hurt. They tied my hands behind me. We walked along the forest trail. We arrived at the river. What could I do? If I persuaded them to untie my hands, I still could not escape. These men were hunters, skilled in using their weapons to kill even small animals. I kneeled on the sand beside the river and prayed.

After some time had passed, Guapitshi became impatient.

"We are wasting our time uselessly," he said. "This no-good person is talking into the wind. Let us return with him to the chief. If the woman is still ill, we will find another way to finish his affair."

"Let us give him sufficient time," Guama said. "The sun is still rising."

While he was yet speaking a child arrived.

"The chief says to bring him to the village."

"Has the woman been healed?" Guama asked.

"The woman has died."

This was the end of everything. My legs were weak. They did not want to carry me back to the village. When we arrived, we found the people stirred up as leaves in a whirlwind. The dead one had been carried on her bed to the roof on sticks. Old women squatted beside her. They patted her cheeks and called her name. Tears ran down their faces as they wailed. Men argued with each other, their voices loud to be heard above the wailing, their eyes flashing with fire. Then two of them took me into my hut and made me sit on the ground in a corner. They tied my hands to a stick of the wall. Then they went out, shut my door and tied it.

I had no strength to weep. I had no strength to pray. I was as an animal, tied, waiting to be sacrificed to appease the anger of departed spirits. I listened to the noises outside. I listened to my breathing and the pounding of my heart. Finally, sleep of weariness caught me. After a time I suddenly awakened. I was not awakened by noise—the noise of storm had ended. I was awakened by stillness. Light still came in beneath the door; it was not the stillness of night.

Then I heard two men talking with each other. Their voices were too weak for me to understand. One seemed to be the voice of the chief; the other I could not recognize. They were not speaking in anger.

After they had spoken for a time, there was silence. Then I heard someone untying my door. It opened, and Guama entered. He did not smile. He pulled his knife from his loincloth and bent over the back of me. I felt the knife moving, cutting. Guama was not killing me. He was cutting the vines which bound me.

"They are calling you," he said.

I stood and rubbed my hurting wrists. Guama let me pass through the door ahead of him. I looked toward the roof on sticks and saw a red cap; then I saw many red caps. Seated in front of them I saw Bula Matadi.

As I arrived, the chief gestured toward me and said to

Bula Matadi, "There he is. He is with strength. We have guarded him well."

Bula Matadi stood to shake my hand.

"Are you well?" he asked.

"I am with strength."

"Do you have a word to send to your wife?"

"I would prefer going to see her."

✿　✿　✿

Storm always drives the child home.

10

Ngalula was well, as I had left her. I did not tell her of the dangers through which I had passed. I did not want her to fear returning with me to work for Jesus in a village of strangers. After the happiness of seeing each other, she gave me two letters. One had arrived a few days ago; it was from Mutombo. 'The other had come long ago; its handwriting was strange.

I unfolded the one from Mutombo and began to read:

Dear brother,

Life to you in the name of Jesus Christ our Saviour. Many days have passed since we left each other. I am happy to tell you of happenings here.

The affairs of our work go well. In this town there are people of two strange tribes; there are also some of our tribemates who have come here to work. When we arrived, we began gathering our tribemates together for worship. Their hearts were thirsty as dry sand to hear the good news. Some accepted Jesus readily; others who come to hear are still caught in sin.

The songs of our believers have begun to do great work for Jesus. A group of singers began to move among the people. Their happy songs drew foreign tribesmen to them. Every Sunday our church house is full of people of all tribes who have come to hear our teaching. There are fourteen grown people whose lives show us that we may call them Christians. I have thirty children who come to class every day. Eight of them now tell me they want to follow Christ.

The affairs at our home are now going well also. When I first arrived, my heart was very discouraged. If God had not given me joy in working with people, I would have stumbled. Then one night God spoke to me in a dream.

I went to sleep while thinking about my problem. In a dream, I was leaving my home village where I had lived for many years. It sat at the bottom of a hill on the edge of a ravine. As I was walking up the hill, I heard a voice call me.

"Mutombo! Mutombo! Don't leave your village. Wait. Look what we have to show you!"

I turned and looked. On the other side of the ravine I saw two men coming down the hill. They were carrying a great heavy cupboard between them. When they arrived at the edge of the ravine they set the cupboard down and opened its doors. From inside it came out many happy, laughing children.

After this dream, I waited at home; I refused thinking about finding another wife. I did not wait for nothing for the stomach of Mbuyi is with child. This is her seventh month and she is well. We are happy. My brother, if this same affair should trouble you, strengthen your heart. God will take care of it.

I don't know when you will receive this letter, but I wanted to tell you these things. If you receive it, write me. Your letter will be as a spring of water to my thirsting soul. Stay well.

Your brother,
Mutombo

To this time, my coming home had brought me affairs of joy. I had found Ngalula well. Mutombo had climbed a big hill and was passing over the top of it; he was happy doing the work of God. If the second letter brought similar words of joy, this would be a good day.

I opened it and read the name of the town—Kinshasa. I turned to its last page and read who had written it—"Your uncles, Tshibuabua and Kabambi." My joy was clouded. I returned to the first page and began reading.

Our relative Mulumba, life to you.

Are you well? Many days have passed since we saw each other. We write you this letter to tell you of affairs which trouble us.

Since you and your father were here, Mvidi Mukulu has made us happy with new children. Each of us has received a baby boy. These new babies, with our other boy children, have given us great responsibility. We must arrange everything necessary so that when they arrive at sufficient age, the affair of bride-price does not trouble them.

We wrote your father to ask him of your affairs. He told us that after you had lived with your wife for a few days, you left her. After many days you have not returned and she continues to sit uselessly.

Our tribemate, when a mother goat chews its grass, its children watch its mouth. You are leaving an example. Younger clansmen are watching you. We helped you with wealth for your wife because you needed it, and because we knew the son of our brother would guard it well. Now is it true that you have deserted your wife? Do you not see that when you do thus, you are despising those who first helped you? This news brings us much distress. More than this, it causes your father shame; it brings great dishonor to the name of our tribe.

There are things clansmen can do to one among them who will not finish his debts. But a dog does not bear its young where people watch it. Please fix up this affair between us quietly, then all of us will be spared shame.

We will be happy to hear that you are living with

your wife, as is the custom. If her sources of birth are locked, there are ancestral medicines to help unlock them. If she is barren, we will be happy to hear that you have done as all men do when a first wife gives them no children.

Do not think that because we are far away you may forget reimbursing our wealth. There are those whom we can send to finish the affair, or if too many days pass, we will come ourselves.

Tell us of your wisdom for finishing this matter. We are waiting for your reply. Stay well.

Your uncles,
Tshibuabua and Kabambi

My only sadness during the following days was because of the words of this letter. When Ngalula asked me about it, I said, "They are troubling me about returning riches." I refused to tell her more. I wrote them that because of the work of Mvidi Mukulu, I could not live with my wife for a time, but that now we were together. I assured them that I was not despising them, and that when the time was sufficient, I would return their wealth.

But for most of the time during those days, I was happy. I wrote Mutombo and rejoiced with him for the good news. I told him of my work at Kele village, and how God had delivered me from death. I told him I feared that his former problem was now troubling me and asked him to pray.

During the hours of evening I went across the river and visited my parents; I sat again with Father at the fire. His heart was not yet opened to accept Christ; like a scar on a tree trunk, it did not change. During the days I rested; I had time to count the good things God had done for us. I rejoiced.

Then they sent me to work in a village again.

"We are not sending you back to Kele," Speaker said. "We

are sending you to another village of the headhunting tribe where they have begun to accept the good news. It is the first village you find when you enter their country. Its name is Kombe. The evangelist left it because of sickness. Ngalula may go with you."

Affairs at Kombe were much better than they had been at Kele. To arrive there was not difficult. The village was on the edge of the headhunters' country. It sat in a cleared-out place just after the path entered the jungle.

The huts and pieces of wall which hooked them together made a closed circle, like at Kele. However the evangelist before me had built a nice house of sticks and mud outside the circle of huts. Near it he had built a class hut. It was a roof on sticks with a low bamboo wall on all its sides. Inside it were rows of large logs with shiny tops, where children had been sitting.

The tribal customs were the same as those at Kele. The grownup people were bound by these customs. They had little hunger for the good news. "It is too late for us to learn of new affairs," they said. "Such affairs are for children."

I was satisfied to teach their children and the children were happy to come. The evangelist before me had done well in winning their friendship. About forty came to class each day. Early every morning some would come to sweep the ground around our house and Ngalula's kitchen hut; then they would sit at the fire, awaiting time for class. When class was finished, other children would go to the stream and carry us gourds full of water on their heads. Nine of the older children had accepted Jesus; I taught them by themselves in a class.

The older people did not show me real friendship, but they did not interfere with my teaching the children. Sometimes a few men would come and squat outside the class shelter while I taught. I would help the children act out things that happened long ago, to remember special days, such as the birthday of Christ. For these meetings, more old people would come. When hunters returned with sufficient meat, they would send Ngalula and me the hip of an animal.

This was the picture of life, months following one after the other, adding up to years. Most of these months brought us great joy. Some of them also brought great trial.

Part of our great joy was to see God working with us. His Spirit opened the children's hearts to love Jesus. Many finished my village class and went to live with other students on the mission post with Speaker and Teacher. Three of the nine I had taught in the class at the beginning were Djari, Mukosa and Ibara. They had finished studying the class of the Book of God. Now they were evangelists in villages of their own people.

We rejoiced for Mutombo and Mbuyi. God gave them first two girls and then a boy.

We rejoiced to see how God protected us. One evening, after the children had gone to their huts, a village elder came and squatted at my fire. We talked about different affairs; our times of talking were separated by times of quiet sitting. I knew something was troubling him inside.

"You have sat with us many days," he finally began. "You have observed our customs, but we have not come to understand yours. Are the customs of your tribe similar to ours?"

"All black people have some customs which are similar, but tribes also have customs which are very different."

"Do you have medicine to guard yourself with, as we do?" he asked.

"Everyone trusts in something or someone whom he believes is sufficient to guard him," I said. "Why do you ask?"

"Because we observe that the medicine with which you protect yourself is very strong."

"What has shown you that my medicine is strong?" I asked.

"Because we have done to you affairs we have done to many others. They died. You are still alive."

"I do not understand. Explain to me."

"We observed that what you were teaching the children caused them to desert the customs of our forefathers. To preserve our tribal customs, we decided to stop your teaching the children. We did not want trouble with Bula Matadi or with your white man. We decided to do away with you and your wife secretly.

"You asked our children to bring coins to give you on the birthday of your Jesus. We made ancestral medicine and rubbed it on the coins so that they would curse the person who received them. The children gave you the coins. You did not die but remained with strength.

"When this failed, we followed other wisdom. We poured poison into your water gourds when the children were returning from the spring. We do not know if you drank the water or if you discarded it. We saw that nothing happened. You and your wife continued with strength.

"Finally, we put poison medicine into something else—something we knew you would not discard. One day hunters returned with a large antelope. We cut off its hip, put poison medicine in it and sent it to you. We know you ate it. The poison did nothing to you. You continued with strength.

"Thus we see that the medicine with which you protect yourself is stronger than the medicine we use to kill. Would you explain to us your kind of medicine? We would like to use it too."

My heart jumped with gratitude and joy. God was

working through us to soften the hearts of the old people, we ourselves not knowing it.

"I do not tie my medicine to my body; I do not keep it under my bed," I told him. I showed him my Testament. "The medicine which guards me is the affair taught in this Book. You keep saying it is an affair for children. Now Mvidi Mukulu has shown all of you that it also takes care of old people. He has shown you that the words of His Book are stronger than the medicine of our forefathers. The teachings of this Book about sin, Jesus and death are the words of the Mvidi Mukulu of all tribes. You must let them enter your hearts. Then this medicine will work for you too."

These months also brought us time of great trial.

Ngalula continued barren. The sadness of this affair grew as the months passed; it made our insides sick. Truly, God had answered our prayers about many things which we knew and which we did not know, but about this affair He was silent.

Without my wanting it thus, my mind would lead me back to affairs of long ago. I could not be happy until I had shown myself and others that I no longer carried a sign of the curse of slavery. I could progress faster than many others by hard work and hard study, but all this helped me little if I continued to be different from all other men because I had no children. Barrenness and slavery were both signs of shame.

These thoughts troubled me when I worked in my field during the day and when I lay on my bed at night. When they had weakened my heart, visitors came to see us. They were waiting for me one afternoon when I returned from the forest. They were my uncles, Tshibuabua and Kabambi.

After eating supper, they began relating the affair which had brought them.

"We have come to talk with you about our wealth which you have eaten," Kabambi began. "We are clansmen of one blood and debts kill friendship. What wisdom do you have for repaying us?"

"I have not yet received suitable wisdom whereby I can finish this affair," I replied.

"Clear up until now? And when do you expect to find such wisdom?"

"This amount of wealth is not near at hand at this time," I continued. "But your wealth is not lost. A debt acknowledged is a debt paid. Truly, I have eaten your wealth, but I have not squandered it."

"You have not squandered it?" Tshibuabua replied. "Are you not squandering it by wasting your years of strength with a woman who can bear you no children? By thus continuing to squander it, you will lose it. Why do you feel that the wisdom followed by our tribemates for generations is unsuitable for you?"

"What wisdom?"

"Stupid. You do not know our tribal customs? Return the woman to her parents. They will reimburse the bride-price and the affair will be finished."

"If you had found me with the waistline of a wasp, you would know that Ngalula has not been feeding me well; you would know that we are having troubles in our house. But we sit together in peace. She has been taking good care of me. Why should I chase her away? Mvidi Mukulu did not teach for man to drive out the woman so that she live like an animal, accepting any male that passes by. He taught that the union of man and woman was never to be broken."

"Does your Mvidi Mukulu teach that you should disrespect your elders?" Kabambi asked. "Does He teach that you should trample their love and help underfoot as a

112

useless thing? Does He tell you to return evil for good? The Mvidi Mukulu you worship is an amazing one!"

"You know yourself that Mvidi Mukulu does not teach such things," I replied. "I do not disrespect you. I will return your things. I am not a thief. Mvidi Mukulu knows why this trouble has caught me. When the time is sufficient, He will help me arrange this affair."

Kabambi continued. "Ask your Mvidi Mukulu to tell you when He feels the time will be sufficient. Ask Him if it will be before our sons arrive at the age of marriage. Or perhaps your Mvidi Mukulu has already decided that our sons will remain bachelors forever?"

"Mvidi Mukulu has shown me many times that He is able to take care of me and my affairs," I replied. "Moreover, what I owe you would not be sufficient for more than the bride-price for one of your sons. Mvidi Mukulu will arrange things."

"You are asking Him to arrange things for you? How can you do this when you do nothing about arranging these affairs yourself?" asked Tshibuabua. "Only crickets sing with their feet; only women bear children. If you refuse to return your wife to her parents and take another, why do you not send her to her mother so that her sources of birth might be unlocked? Is this affair too hard for you?"

My uncles were referring to a shameful custom whereby a mother keeps her daughter from getting a baby-stomach until the time of her marriage. When I read God's Book I learned that this custom was sinful and useless. I did not want to anger them more by telling them so.

"Listen, my uncles," I said. "I asked you to help pound my corn, but does that make the pestle yours? I chose Ngalula, I married her, I live with her. Is it not my affair what I do with her?"

"Not your affair alone," Tshibuabua continued. "Our

custom says she is also our affair because you purchased her with our wealth. Mulumba, why do you cause us such anguish? What gives you such a hard head? Stop being stupid. Follow the affairs of our tribe which will enable you to finish your duty. As the elders say, If need be, eat with a knife. Our tribal law binds you to do whatever is necessary."

"You will not enslave me with tribal customs," I said. "If my heart tells me tribal customs are wrong. I'll never be bound with them until frogs grow feathers."

"What?" Tshibuabua jumped to his feet and shook his fist angrily. "Have you no fear of shame? Do you not know that he who is troubled with shame will be troubled with hunger? How can you spit upon the inheritance of your father? How can you have the brazenness to so offend us?"

"Sit down, Tshibuabua. Restrain yourself. A bean planted in anger will not sprout. Let us do him no harm." Kabambi pulled him to his seat and then spoke to me.

"Mulumba, our anger is truly great, but we restrain it so we can talk with you. It appears we are wasting our time uselessly. Do not think that we left our work and spent money for this long journey to find you, for nothing. You are sending us away empty-handed. You refuse to promise to do anything that will bring us back our wealth. You leave us no other path. Bula Matadi has established laws whereby debtors are judged. We are taking this affair to him. You have a few days to change your mind. After that, expect the arrival of a soldier who will arrest you and bring you to judgment."

I could not believe his words. "I'm sorry it must be thus," I said. "It is not safe for you to travel at night. Sleep here. In the morning you will eat and leave."

They slept, ate and left with few words. I could not sleep. I could not eat. I too spoke few words. But inside me there

114

was war. During the whole day which followed, two voices fought each other. When I wanted to sleep that night, the fighting continued.

I rose from my bed and walked about, outside the village wall. I listened to the arguing within me. Why did not God answer our cries? Why could He not give me the promise of answering by means of a dream, as He had done for Mutombo? Was Mutombo better than I? God had delivered me from great trouble before. Was He deserting me this time?

It would be easy to send Ngalula to her parents, to thus recover the bride-price, and marry again. Then this yoke would be off my neck.

Then what would happen to Ngalula? What hope would there be of her staying in the path of Jesus? And what evil had she done to deserve being put away? If I sent her into a path which would ruin her life, how would my heart give me rest for all the days ahead of me? How would I justify myself before God?

It would be better to keep Ngalula, and to seek bride-price for another wife who could bear me children. Ngalula would not be forced into a life of sin, and my uncles would stop pestering me for I would have done something toward recovering their wealth.

But a man of many wives must divide his love into many little loves. And men with two wives are not permitted to work for Christ.

But had not Christ put the desire within me to work for Him? If He wanted me to continue in His work, why did He not heal Ngalula's body and give us children? If He did not want to do this for me, what other path was left for me to follow?

If I took a second wife, I would quit the work of Jesus, leave this village of foreign tribesmen and return to sit

115

among my own people. My own tribemates would better respect me. When my uncles visited me, had not the words of Kabambi shown me how I was shaming Mvidi Mukulu by trampling their love underfoot and returning evil for good?

This is what I would have to do. I would have to take a second wife. But I would still give Ngalula her rightful place in our home. If you marry a young girl as a second wife, they say, don't neglect your first one; her wisdom and your wisdom are the same length, because you've grown up together.

If someday God judged me for doing something which forced me out of His work, I would ask Him to explain why He did not answer prayer and give us children so I could stay in His work. The name of God would not be shamed before my tribemates. They would respect me as a person among them again. Thus this sign of curse would be taken off me and I would stand proudly among them as a man. I strengthened my heart to go tell Ngalula.

I returned to our house. I looked at Ngalula, lying quietly on her bed. I decided not to ruin her night of rest. I would tell her in the morning.

❊   ❊   ❊

Even a champion will fail in some things.

11

I heard the first cock crow. It was still dark. As I lay quietly pictures began passing by the eyes of my mind. Some of them came from my thinking, some of them came from my dreams. My thinking was telling me that this was the day I would begin following the new path I had chosen. My dreams showed me a path leading up a high steep hill. I had to follow that path up the hill, but my legs hurt with weakness. I fell to the ground. I struggled, dragging myself up the hill, until my mind told me that morning light had come.

I chased the dream picture from my mind and opened my eyes. It was time to tell Ngalula. I strengthened my heart, and turned myself over in my bed. I looked at her bed. It was empty. She had already gone.

I put on my clothes and went outside. One of my class children was sweeping my compound. Two others had started a fire and were warming themselves.

"Have you seen Ngalula?" I asked them.

"Yes, Teacher. She got a basket in the kitchen hut and went to your field," they said.

I sat down on a stool by the fire. I watched the children. I thought to myself, Why do they come by themselves to my house every morning? Besides sitting in my class, they come sit at my house. The time they pass with me is much; the time they pass with their parents is little. Why is this? Because their parents are so busy with the affairs of grownups that they don't have time for the affairs of children? Sometimes, when parents are busy with their grownup affairs, they drive their children away.

So the children don't play in the yards of the mothers who bore them. They come sit with me and call me Teacher. They count me as their real father. I pass much time with them and they love me.

But in a few days I will be leaving these children, I told myself. Then who will have time for them? Will they still come sweep my compound, the house being empty? To whom will they show their love?

That is the business of their parents, I told myself. How could parents who had borne these children in joy, now let them run around uselessly, unloved? This was sinful.

Was it only the business of the parents? Was it not also my business? How could the parents see, when their minds were as dark with evil as the deep jungle? I lived in the light of Jesus Christ, bright and shining. Now I would follow in the footsteps of the parents. I too would turn my back on these children. I would neglect them. Truly, Jesus loved them; He had died for them. But I would let them be lost forever. Could it be thus? Who would carry greater guilt—I or their parents? The insides of Ngalula and me, were they not sick to have children? What were these who loved us so greatly? Were they not children? Thus I saw that the new path I had wanted to follow was surpassingly sinful.

It was good that Ngalula had gone to the field. As yet, she knew nothing of my battle. She was a good wife. I would not tell her of what I had wanted to do. God had shown me something new. Mutombo had said that the joy he found working with people had kept him from stumbling. Could it not keep me from stumbling too? As Mutombo had urged me, I would keep believing that God would cut the path ahead of us.

118

Ngalula and I were not barren. We had many children. They were more truly our children than they were their parents' children. The joy of bearing a child in our bodies would be great, but we would have the happiness of bearing children for Jesus. This was not bearing bodies; this was bearing souls which would live with Him forever.

I did not tell Ngalula of this time of testing which almost made me stumble. I did tell her that her barrenness would not kill our marriage. I asked her to help me, that we bear as many children as we could for Christ. Together, our hearts were established. I decided that if a soldier came because of my debt, I would not fear. Many Christians had been thrown into prison before me.

No soldier came. I heard no more word from my uncles for many days. In the months that followed, Ngalula and I found happiness we had not yet known. When the time came for us to leave Kombe, many of the class children were reading the Book of God to their parents. Twenty children and four of their mothers were following Jesus Christ.

Speaker had begun a school on the mission post to train shepherds of the Christian flock. He asked that either Mutombo or I enter this school. Mutombo now had five children; he had made larger fields to feed and clothe them. If he left his work and his fields to come to school, he would have no means of feeding his family.

Family burdens did not hinder me. I entered the school and studied hard for three years. Ngalula learned many things in class which helped her make us a home which we were proud for others to see. We rejoiced that God was recompensing us with affairs of joy which He had kept hidden from us—affairs those who had children could not enjoy.

When I finished my studies, mission elders placed their hands on my head, making me a shepherd, or pastor.

Ngalula and I were sent to shepherd the flock of believers who lived at the city of Makala, working for the white men who mined diamonds there.

My footprints had now arrived at an important crossing of paths. Behind me was the little footpath, coming out of the village of Kombe. Ahead of me was the big path which led to the big work which waited for us at the city of Makala. As I planned for what was ahead I remembered how many things had changed in my country while I had traveled to this crossroad.

Since my childhood, affairs in our country had become turned around, as a caterpillar changes around to a butterfly. By this time, men named Bula Matadi were scattered throughout our country. All of our people were now under his authority. Laws were established. Each Bula Matadi had black people as his secretaries, messengers and soldiers. They helped him enforce these laws. Because people of all tribes feared these laws, they sat together in peace.

There were laws telling us what not to do. A man could not steal, either by cleverness or by violence. He could not spread lies about his neighbor. He could not enter into his neighbor's yard to cause trouble. He could not ruin by force the purity of a young girl. If a person did any of these things he was pursued by soldiers as dogs follow the scent of prey. He was caught and judged. If he was guilty he would pay a big fine or be thrown into prison. Everybody learned to respect the lives and things of others.

There were laws telling us what we must do. Every year every man who did not live and work in a city was to make a field and care for it. Every year every man paid Bula Matadi a sum of tax money. Every married man was to have the name of his wife written into his tax book. If he refused to take good care of his wife he was caught and judged.

Because people sat in peace, one could travel wherever he

120

pleased without fear. There were many ways to travel. Many steamboats went up and down our rivers. Where there were not rivers large enough for steamboats, iron paths were made for steam machines of noise called trains. But for many villages in the jungle or grassland, there were neither train paths or rivers for boats. For these villages, Bula Matadi made paths wide enough for little houses of iron sitting on wheels called machine motorcars, or such machines with large boxes to carry things, called trucks. He paid villagers to take care of the roads. If they failed, he disciplined them.

Laws were enforced. There was peace. We were making fields. We could travel easily. Because of these things wealth grew rapidly.

Our forefathers were wise as sages. Their proverbs are the palm oil with which we eat words and thus understand life. They said, While prosperity is near call it to yourself, lest after it has passed you weep in poverty. Thus we of our tribe worked hard to gather wealth.

We made large fields of rice, corn, peanuts, manioc and cotton. White men came and planted fields of cocoa, coffee, rubber and oil palms. Things from the fields were sold. Traders carried them down the machine roads to the cities; here these things were put onto trains or boats and were taken to foreign countries.

Other white men came to our country and set up stores. Those who like honey will find the path to the beehive. We habitually went to these stores to see all the new things which kept coming. We used our money to buy the things our hearts desired.

We could buy many kinds of cloth. Thus our customs of things we wore changed. When I was a child, my loincloths were always blue. There was no other kind of cloth. Now there was cloth with stripes, spots and pictures. Cloth with

121

colors that appeared weak and sick began to disappear and cloth of colors which made our eyes happy began to appear—colors of the flowers, the grassy hills, the sky. Then there came cloth which was soft and bright-colored, which one could wear and wash for many days. It was called "wax." Its price was hard, but every woman with a dress of such cloth wore it with pride. Everyone who saw her wearing it knew that her husband loved her.

In the stores, we could buy things to eat. Thus our customs of eating became changed. When I was a child, we were happy for a bit of dried salted fish for meat. People began to despise this fish when in the stores they found fish locked inside metal cups. Soon such cupped fish was scorned as cupped meat of other animals began to appear. Then as wealth grew, people wanted to despise all meat locked in cups and began craving freshly killed meat. A person with guests was especially honored if he could feed them freshly cooked cow meat.

There is one thing we customarily eat every day. Corn and manioc flours are stirred into boiling water until it becomes heavy and stiff. Then it is rolled into a round white loaf, which fits into the eating bowl. This loaf is called "bidia." We eat it, breaking off pieces of the loaf with our fingers.

During the years of my childhood, we ate bidia with cooked greens and salted fish perhaps twice a day. We were happy. But now it was our custom to also eat beans and peanuts and rice, and fruits like bananas, pineapples and oranges in their seasons. In the stores they begged us to buy oatmeal, milk, sugar, bread, margarine, cookies and hard candy.

Thus people looked upon anyone wearing a blue loincloth and eating bidia and dried fish with scorn and contempt. A respectful person wore trousers, a shirt and shoes. At important times he also wore stockings, a tie and a coat. If he were feeding guests, he would prepare bidia, fresh meat and other good things.

In the stores we found things to wear, things to eat and other things as well. We found soft bed blankets, mattresses, pretty cloths to cover our tables, glass for windows and kerosene lamps which burned brightly. We found sewing machines, bicycles, radios which caught the voices of men passing in the air and motorcycles which we named after their sound, "tuku-tuku."

When I thought of these things, I remembered the promises the first Bula Matadi had made to Father and his friends so many years ago. Now I saw with my own eyes that these promises were coming true. But there was something else I began seeing with my eyes which troubled me.

We rejoiced because of laws which made evildoers afraid. We rejoiced for peace and for wealth. We played with the new things we found in our hands, as children play with new toys. Give a begging child a grasshopper, they say, and he'll stop complaining. And so we saw that Bula Matadi kept giving us new grasshoppers, thus stretching out the days of our childhood, lest we grow to be as tall as he.

While the years passed, many more missionaries came. They established their posts everywhere among larger tribes. They built for themselves houses of stone or burnt brick with iron roofs. They traveled between their posts or among our villages in motorcars or trucks. Whenever more missionaries came, they brought with them new things which they believed would help them teach better, such as horns which shouted their words loudly to be heard by people far away and light machines which showed walking pictures at night. They also brought new kinds of things for themselves which they believed would make their lives happier.

Missionary doctors healed the sick. Missionary nurses helped them. Then doctors working for Bula Matadi appeared. Working together with missionary doctors, they made war on sicknesses which had killed so many of our people in the years which had passed. They built houses for healing and houses for bearing children called "hospitals." In towns too small for hospitals, they established medicine houses and paid nurses they had trained to live there and care for the sick. The number of healing houses was sufficient so that people living in almost any village of our country could get help if bad sickness caught them.

Missionary teachers established schools which taught a variety of things. White men of Bula Matadi helped them with wealth and with wisdom. The affair of teaching grew until children in almost all of the villages of our country could finish five years of studying.

The path which led to the big work that waited for us at the city of Makala meant a new way of living for Ngalula and me. More than five thousand people lived in this city. Many of them sat in more than one hundred houses white men had built for their workmen. These people were from many different tribes. I was the only pastor among them. The open doors of working for God surpassed my strength to enter them.

One or two days each week I went to the hospital, which had places for three hundred sick people. I went from bed to bed, praying with people and talking to them about Christ. Other days I tied my Bible, hymn book, and note-taking book onto the back of my bicycle. I rode to visit people who lived in nearby villages. I glorified God with my large strong body. It sent me on long journeys. If my bicycle became old and died from going on many journeys, I would buy repair pieces to fix it until I could buy a new one. When I taught I did not respect one tribe above another. I had a face of happiness for everybody.

At Makala Ngalula also had much work to do. She used the things she had learned in class while I was studying to be a pastor. At Kombe she could do little work with the women. But here the women followed after her, begging for help. We divided the city into parts, so that she could have women's meetings at different places on different days of each week.

Her meetings drew women from many different tribes who had a common heart to learn. When they gathered she first taught them a lesson that helped them take better care of their homes and families. Then she taught them from the Bible. After working like this for many years people of many different tribes and villages came to love us. They would meet together and worship with joy. Our teaching tied them together as one and the number of those who loved our Lord Jesus grew exceedingly.

Our work among people was bigger and our work at home progressed better too.

The white-man doctor at the hospital had come to the end of his wisdom for helping Ngalula and had failed. But because she had no children to care for at home, she was able to help me work in the fields. You can tell by watching the tree when it is time to start picking mangoes. We saw that the trees around us were ripe to bear wealth.

With our hoes we turned up grassland soil and planted things which would grow there. With a jungle knife and an axe we cleaned ground in the forest and planted some coffee trees. Each year we enlarged the space and planted a few more trees. They began to bear fruit.

What they paid me for being a pastor and what we received from selling things from our fields was more than enough. When a few years had passed, I sent much of the money I had saved to my uncles at Kinshasa. It was only about one-tenth of my debt, but Tshibuabua and Kabambi would be happy to receive it; they would not trouble me for a while.

When I had worked hard some more years, I gathered sufficient money to buy a small mill and motor with which to grind manioc and corn flour. In matters of money, the mill helped us much. When I ground flour for other people for a year, I was able to send money to Kinshasa a second time. We were progressing well now. We could see it with our eyes. We were lightening our debt-burden bit by bit. If I kept progressing this way I could pay the whole debt in eight more years. I hoped we could continue like this forever.

A missionary moved to Makala. He began building his post a few kilometers up the path leading out of the city. He pressed and burned clay bricks. With some of them he built his post houses. He brought other brick to where we lived. Our Christian women helped him during the days; our Christian men helped him in the afternoons when their work in the mines was finished.

First they built a large house for worshiping God. Then they built a house for their pastor. They fastened on roofs of iron; on the ground they poured floors of cement. Ngalula and I began to sit in our new house. We said farewell to houses of stick and mud with roofs of grass. We didn't want to sit in such houses again forever.

While doing my work of a pastor, I came to know men who worked in the offices of the diamond mine. They had studied higher classes and had become wealthy. I heard them whispering of affairs which had already passed in our country, the people of today not seeing them with their eyes. The affairs these men were showing each other made me want to be afraid. I feared their whisperings would split the house into pieces. They were young men who had tired of eating grasshoppers. They were talking about a new idea—an idea which was sweeping across our country swiftly as a dry-season wind. They were talking about a new word I'd never heard before—"dipanda."

* * *

When a man is poor, he sees today and lives for tomorrow; when he becomes rich, he forgets yesterday, and lives for today.

12

"Beya, my son, is entering marriage next Saturday," tribemate Kongolo informed me one day. "You must come to the wedding feast. Bring Ngalula."

Kongolo and his wife came to our house for worshiping God nearly every Sunday. His age passed mine by a few years. For all of his working years he had been at the diamond mines. His son, Beya, had studied higher classes at Kinshasa. Now he was working as a secretary to the white chief of the diamond mining company.

"This is not a Christian marriage," I said. "Many important people will be there." Neither his son nor the woman were true followers of Jesus.

"Are you not an important person among us?" he replied. "I will send my younger brother with his motorcar to get you. He will arrive about two o'clock in the afternoon."

Saturday morning arrived. Ngalula went to a neighbor's. There she sat under a tree in the yard, her lady friend fixing her hair. I ironed my nicest black trousers until they were flat, like a well-worn footpath. When the sun was straight up, we went into our bedroom to begin dressing for the wedding feast.

"Is your heart shaking, Ngalula? Are you ready to go sit among big people today?"

"I will be with you, but I will not talk," she said. "The wren rejoices in her own nest; when she is in another's, she sits with a stiff neck."

Ngalula opened the rubber cloth bag which guarded our

best clothing from dust and took out her dress of wax cloth.

"Did you know that Beya is of our tribe," I said, "and the girl he is marrying is of our former masters' tribe? Look how God has turned things around!"

"Yes. Those who long ago were fighting each other are now marrying each other," she replied. "But should we be surprised? The seed we've been planting these many years, should it not be sprouting?"

"We have seen it sprouting before our eyes," I said. "In Father's day, men of the other tribe were making war on us. But it is no longer thus. We walk with each other, we work with each other, we worship with each other, we even marry each other. God has truly done great work among us. He has almost erased the lines which divided us."

Ngalula, already dressed, sat on the bed mattress to slip her feet into skinny shoes on high-built heels—shoes for seeing, not for walking.

"Have you noticed something else which God has turned around?" I continued. "Today, who are the most important helpers of Bula Matadi? Who have finished higher classes and are now doing the work of chiefs in the diamond mining company? Who are the clerks, receiving higher salaries, working in the white men's stores? Are they not men of our tribe? It appears that our being caught as slaves has turned around to be a good affair. The desire to cover shame gave birth to lust—lust for power, for glory, for wealth. Thus God has turned things around so that we are now masters over those who once had enslaved us!"

"Mulumba, hush! Don't you know that cockroaches, though they have their heads hidden in the grass roof, know all that is going on in the house? Let words like this remain inside our bedroom. If they spread among people outside, they would split the house into two pieces!"

I was tying my tie, but shot an eye at Ngalula. She was now standing before the looking glass. When I saw her, my eyes became thirsty. Truly, Ngalula's body had grown heavier with the passing of years, but her beauty had not disappeared. Her hair had been divided into small bunches. Each bunch was wrapped tightly with black thread. These wrapped-up bunches looked like clean rows of tiny black palm trees. She was enclosing them by carefully wrapping a silk bandana around her head. The dress of red and yellow flowers on blue, her neck and cheeks which shined clean and smooth, her chin lifted upwards showing she was brave, her nicely fixed hair and bright-colored headcloth—God of love, I said in my heart, Why have you done me so well? I, a grownup man of many years, still feel the happiness of youth!

When we got out of the motorcar at Kongolo's house, we saw that we were truly with important people. At home we felt like we had put on exceedingly good clothes; now we felt like we were wearing clothes of every day. Women were proudly showing their dresses which sparkled with gold-colored thread, dresses with borders of long loose threads which swung as they turned their bodies this way and that. Then I saw Beya's young friends who had come from Kinshasa. I did not know that there was such nice-looking clothing under the sun. They looked as if they were children of the same father with Bula Matadi. To protect their eyes from the sun, they had covered them with dark-colored glasses, as Bula Matadi did.

Kongolo and his friends welcomed us with joy. We greeted Beya and his wife. We shook hands and spoke words of friendship with white men, their wives and other guests. Then they showed us to chairs where we sat with others, waiting until the food was prepared.

About half of Kongolo's front yard, from his house to the

fence, was covered with a roof. A flat roof frame was covered with fresh green palm branches. Beneath this roof in the shade, were three tables side by side, each of them one length with the roof. Along the sides of the tables were long bench seats. The tables and benches were made of bamboo, which lasts for few days, but which may be easily tied together in this fashion. Women were preparing the food on fires behind the house.

Guests continued arriving—some guests with whom Kongolo and his son worked at the mines, some from far away—until the number of them was so great that a falling leaf would not find a path to the ground. People greeted each other, their whole bodies rejoicing. They laughed, with eyes closed, mouths open wide, their teeth shining. They clasped and shook four hands. They slapped each others' backs. Almost everybody there was of one of two tribes: either of my tribe, or of the tribe which had once ruled over us; but here everybody was showing happiness. All faces were with big smiles. No one could see that anything divided us. We were one.

Cooking ladies put plates, knives and forks along the edges of the tables. Then along the lengths of them, the women put white covered bowls of food. People quieted down. Kongolo asked me to thank Mvidi Mukulu for the food and for the happiness of this day. Beya and his wife sat down at the middle of the first table, their backs to the house. His friends sat down at either of his hands. Then all other guests found places, the men unfolding their white handkerchiefs and sitting on them to protect their trousers.

There were bowls of soft brown beans; finely-pounded greens with tiny bits of red pepper; rice, shining golden-colored with oil; cut-up pieces of pineapple, sitting in their juice; big pieces of cooked cow meat, their corners sticking out of warm sweet-smelling sauce of palm oil; and bidia. For

131

meat for this many people, I knew Kongolo had spent a month's wages to buy a cow.

Here a loaf of bidia was gray and rough, because the flour had not been well dried or sufficiently ground, there a loaf of bidia had set too long, and had become cool and heavy. In such cases, the loaves were discarded. Other loaves were brought in their places, steaming hot and white.

When people finished eating, things to drink were brought. There was one box of bottles with orange drink and many boxes of white man's corn wine, called beer. While we were drinking, drums began beating. Six musicians—two with marimbas, four with drums—began to play for dancing. The drums began softly, as one runs with light feet; then they became louder, as the runner trying to speed up pounds his feet to the ground. Their throbbing became as a thousand hearts beating at the same time, their rhythm filling the bones and flesh, the trees, the sun, the air we breathed.

Then the marimbas joined them, making melodies that would not let people rest, melodies that lifted their bodies off the benches and moved them into the dance, twisting, turning, as snakes uncoiling together. Players beat their instruments with fury, their faces wet with sweat lifted toward the sun—faces twisted with the suffering of joy—faces showing their hearts were drunk with the wine of happiness. When bodies wearied, they would stop for a time and become like all other people again, drinking, talking, laughing with those near them.

When the sun began to lower, the white men and their wives put their empty glasses on the table, wished Beya and his wife happiness once more and left.

Young tribemates from Kinshasa watched them leave. Then they said, "We see that you are still eating friendship with the white man here."

"Yes," our people replied.

"It is no affair. Have friendship with them while they are here. They will not remain with us many more days."

"What do you mean?" our home people asked.

"Have you people in small villages not heard what is happening in our country?" the big-city people asked. "We are asking for dipanda. We want to be on top of the affairs of our country. We want to be chiefs of ourselves."

"Do you truly see us ruling ourselves?" said one of our former masters' tribe. "That is stupid thinking. He who eats danger will kill himself. There are no black men among us with sufficient wisdom to rule over us."

"Thus you agree with the white Bula Matadi who has been calling us heathen, imbeciles, monkeys? What day did you measure our intelligence? Are you using pretty words of mouth to offend us? How do we know we don't have sufficient intelligence unless the white man will let us try to rule ourselves?"

People were gathering around the speakers, thick as blades of grass. They packed themselves together tightly to hear. A young man of my own tribe from Kinshasa drank the beer that was left in his glass and stood upon a chair, speaking loudly.

"Life to you!"

"Uhhhhhhh—" the people responded.

"Life to you!"

"Uhhhhhhh—"

All was quietness. The air was tight, like a bowstring pulled to throw an arrow.

"You people in little villages say, 'Let us sit with the white man longer; let us give him more time.' He has already sat with us for fifty years. Is that not enough time? All these years having passed, he has not yet taught us the first class of how to rule ourselves. Will he ever teach us to rule ourselves? No!

"He has done many good things for us. Why is he feeding us these good things? He is feeding the mother goat pretty green sugar leaves so she stands still while he milks her dry. Shall we accept for it to be thus forever? Why should he take our diamonds and copper to make himself rich, we remaining poor? Why should he by himself make laws for a country full of black people? Why should he, a white man, tell the countries of the whole world our affairs of happiness and our affairs of trouble?

"My friends, the days have arrived when we must speak of these things. The sun will shine on those who stand before it shines on those who kneel. These are days when we must answer the questions of why we walk around under the sun. We must shout out the answer loudly, so that the earth, the sky, the whole world can hear it."

"Thus you are saying, Let us drive the white man out," someone asked.

"All these years the white man has been using our drumsticks to make music for his dance. If the drumsticks hit him in the eye and stop the music, it is not the fault of our drum, it is the fault of his beating. He has refused to teach us to rule ourselves. If he does not change we will chase him out."

"Stupid wisdom," someone grumbled. "Can a red ant catch an elephant by the tusks?"

"A goat always wants to skin the shins of its master," said another.

"You are saying we are too weak to rule over the elephant? Do not little red ants carry off the tops of mushrooms? You people are the stupid ones. You are happy to let the elephant crush us under his feet forever, never complaining? Doesn't the white man have any of his own

134

people in the world he can rule over, that he must always rule over us? This country is of black people! The white man's days here are finished. White man, go home!"

The young man came down off the chair. Most of the drinking glasses were empty. The bottles were empty. The dancing had stopped. The music had stopped. All the people had come to hear what the young men were saying. There were no longer smiles of happiness. Now fire flashed in the eyes of men. They grumbled; they argued. Women shot their eyes here and there in fear.

Then another young man stood onto the chair. He was of our former masters' tribe. His words rolled from his mouth like wheels well oiled. He used his swinging arms as hammers, to nail down his words.

"Life to you!"

"Uhhhhhhh—"

Again the tight air—and terrible quietness, when even the scratching of a hen in dry leaves sounded like thunder.

"We have heard the words of our friend. The white man is still with us. He has done much to help us. He is our father; we are his child. Why should a girl who has not yet reached puberty be looking for a midwife? With our feet in water, why are we crying for thirst? Do you see that the white man's work is finished? He has built, but he has not finished. A house with an unfinished roof is like a woman without breasts. What is it good for?"

He waited for the water of his words to soak into dry ears. Then he continued.

"Our friend spoke words from his mouth. But he didn't tell us everything. He guarded other words within him. I relate to you a fable. It will explain to you the real words that are in his heart.

"Mr. Turtle tired of being a despicable animal which no one noticed. He wanted to be important. He heard that the birds were going to have a feast in the sky. He asked the birds if he could go with them.

" 'No,' the birds said. 'Why should you try to do something you are not sufficient to do? You cannot join us in the sky until you sprout wings. If you try before then, trouble will catch you.'

"But the turtle's stomach was empty and he craved to be a big chief. He said, 'It is true that I have never before done this kind of thing. But when the day of the feast comes, if you each will loan me two feathers, I will rise up off the ground and fly with you.'

"When the day of the feast arrived, they met at the taking-off place. The birds each loaned the turtle two feathers. He held them in his hands and feet. When the birds took off, the turtle began waving his feathers. His body lifted up off the ground and he flew with the birds.

"While they were flying, Mr. Turtle said, 'You know, when people go to great feasts such as this one, they give themselves new names. My new name will be "You-All." '

"The birds did not want to be shamed by saying that they had never heard of such a custom; they respected the wisdom of the turtle who was much older than they. So they each took a new name.

"When they arrived at the place of the feast, the man of the sky was very happy to see them. Most of all, he was happy to see Mr. Turtle. He put him at the head of the table; he made him chief of the feast.

"Mr. Turtle was very happy. Bowls of good things to eat were brought and placed on the table. Then Mr. Turtle asked, 'Excuse me, sir, but for whom did you prepare all these good things?'

" 'Why, for you all.'

" 'That's my name,' the turtle said. 'He made these things for me. Now you birds must wait while I eat first.'

136

"The turtle ate until his stomach wanted to split his shell. There were only scraps of things left. Then he told the birds, 'Now it is time for you to eat.'

" 'We will eat, truly?' the birds replied. 'After you have left us scraps? Why do you make yourself chief where you're not supposed to be chief? Why are you ruining the feast for all of us? We will not eat. We are going back to earth.'

"The birds left, one by one. When each one passed Mr. Turtle, he took two feathers. Mr. Turtle begged them to show him mercy, but they refused. After they had left, Mr. Turtle let go of the sky and came crashing down to the earth. He did not die, but his shell broke into pieces, as we see it is today."

There was silence. Then someone shouted, "What is your fable telling us?"

The speaker stood quietly, his heart asking his eyes if he should reply.

"Explain the wisdom hidden in your fable," men cried with anger. "What are you saying?"

"I'm saying that people of your tribe see that the time has come for us to have independence. You say it is because the white man has treated us badly. It is not thus. You want dipanda in order that you can be chiefs over us. Is it not true? Doing thus will ruin the feast of all of us. You did not rule over us long ago. You will not rule over us now. If this is your wisdom we'll drive you out from among us. We'll break your back and you'll carry the scars of your shame, time never ending."

Men growled like angry lions. Some clenched their fists. Others took off their dark glasses and put them in their coat pockets. Others spoke words of hot anger. Hands grabbed the clothing of the speaker, pulling him to the ground. Men began opening their mouths, pouring fire onto each other.

They offended, they threatened, the noise of their voices rising like a growing storm. I heard scuffling of feet among those standing and then the sound of fists striking flesh. I quickly caught Ngalula's arm and found the younger brother of Kongolo.

"I see the time is sufficient for us to leave," I said. "Would you take us home?"

❊ ❊ ❊

The tongue of the mouth sends tribes to war.

13

Dipanda. What a strange word. For all these many years we had been pouring the medicine of the good news onto the hatreds which once divided us. We thought these wounds in peoples' hearts had almost healed. What kind of power was inside this single word which tore open the wounds again in one day?

I could not find the answer to this question now. I did not have time. Word reached me that Father was very ill.

Ngalula and I found room on a trader's truck that was going to my home village of Luaba. When we arrived, we learned that Father had been ill two weeks. He had aged much. His body was wasted and tired.

Relatives who lived nearby had already arrived. Word had been sent to my brother, Mutombo, my sister, Ndaya, and my uncles at Kinshasa. Mutombo arrived the same day I did. We had not seen each other for many years. The desire of our hearts was to sit up all night and tell each other all the things that had happened in our lives. But first we had to look after Father.

We could not carry him to the hospital at the mission post across the river, his body was too weak. We called the white-man doctor. He came and looked at Father. When he was about to leave we went to ask him some questions.

"How did you find him?"

"I must tell you plainly. He is very ill."

"Might he recover?"

"I left pills with your mother. They will make his suffering less. That is the one thing I can do to help him."

When we understood we could do nothing to help Father's body, we decided we must try to help his soul. We took our Bibles and went into the house. We squatted beside him, where he lay on the mat. We watched him quietly. Then Mutombo spoke.

"Father, the sickness is strong."

Father grunted.

"If you should disappear from among us, where would you go?"

After a pause he replied, "I would return to Mvidi Mukulu who created me."

Mutombo waited a bit and then said, "When a leopard fulfills its days of wandering, it returns to its den. All the days of your life, Father, you have been a leopard of strength to us."

Father grunted.

"But any person in his wandering upon earth does things which displease Mvidi Mukulu. It would be good for you to arrange these affairs with Him before you go to see Him."

"I am not a bad person."

"You have been a good father. You have cared for us well. But there is no person on earth who has not sinned. For this reason, Mvidi Mukulu sent His Son to help us. Because of His Son, we can eat a covenant of peace with Mvidi Mukulu. When we die, we can sit with Him forever in happiness."

Father rested a bit. Then he spoke again. "That story was brought to us by the white man. The bad things he has done are troubling his heart. He could not return to Mvidi Mukulu without a helper."

"But Father, as Mvidi Mukulu created all of us, He sent His Son to help all of us. The bow and arrow must help each

140

other if they are to kill the elephant. How can you go sit in happiness with Mvidi Mukulu if you reject the One He sent to help you? Will you arrive at His village with your own strength?"

Talk was weakening Father. He rested a bit. Then he spoke again. We had to listen closely to hear him.

"I have trusted the Mvidi Mukulu of our forefathers all the days of my life. I have always sacrificed to the spirits of my ancestors, as is our custom, that they not be angry with me. They have treated me well. Now I arrive at the end of my life. You ask me to forsake the way of our forefathers. You ask me to offend the spirits of my ancestors. You want me to stop believing the way I always have and accept the way of a stranger. What would my ancestral spirits think of me? What would they do to me? This is no time to think of new things. I shall die as my forefathers died. I need nothing more."

We wanted to say more, but we saw that Father could not talk longer. We wanted to take hold of his soul with our hands, that it not escape. We longed for him to open his ears and listen until he could believe. But it was too late. Father's heart was as dried skin—skin which would never soften, though it be pounded with water in a mortar. Mutombo took his hand and prayed aloud. Then we arose and left, weeping in our hearts.

Father died, as those before him had died. As is the custom, our relatives grieved like people whose minds have been broken. As is the proverb, When an old chief dies, there is nothing left to lean upon; fear takes his place. Mourners undressed, except for waist cloths. They clasped each other, weeping aloud. They fell onto the ground and rolled in grief. They threw dust into the air, letting it fall upon their bodies. They sat on the ground wailing, rocking their bodies this way and that.

The affairs of Jesus Christ had divided our family in life; now it divided us in death. When the wailing became less, the mourners noticed Mutombo, Ngalula and me. We were fully dressed, sitting to one side on chairs, weeping quietly.

One approached us and said, "Why aren't you mourning? Did you not love our father? Don't you have any shame to sit there like that? If you don't mourn his death, will guests mourn? How contemptuous! Now you have shown us plainly the cruelty that is in your hearts!"

Another said, "As you are refusing to mourn with us, thus you will also refuse to help us arrange the path for Father's spirit to go rest at Kaloba Nduaya. Is it not so?"

Our people believe that when a good person dies, his spirit wanders here and there, hunting for the path which leads to Kaloba Nduaya, the place of rich, red earth where banana and plantain trees grow in abundance and where happinesses never end. The living must help him get there. The people of his family must put money inside the mat which encloses his body so he can pay to be ferried across the rivers. They must put bidia and meat in a pot on his grave for him to eat while he is on his journey. They must put his pots and dishes on his grave and break them, so only he can use them. If he finds that the living have not given him these things, he will return and torment them.

"Father's soul has already finished its journey," Mutombo replied. "It has returned to Mvidi Mukulu. The time of helping him has already passed."

"How has it already passed?" they cried. "Don't you know that your refusal to follow this path will pull down a curse upon all of us who remain? What sufferings will catch us, you acting like this? How can you torment us thus? Our hearts already being turned to water by sadness, you spit upon us! This sadness has passed us up to bear. It would crush the heart of a lion."

142

And they returned to wailing, more loudly than before.

"We have sadness too," Mutombo said as they paused to listen. "We have sadness which passes up your minds to understand. We loved our father. We weep for him. But more than that, we weep for you. You are yet alive. You are tormented by fears, fears that the Son of God was sent to take away from us. But your hearts remain closed to His path. You yourselves do not yet know the path of joy our father could have known. Take warning in time, the elders have said, or the earth and the termites will remind you of your foolishness. Your sorrow for Father will pass, but our sorrow for you remains."

Mother fulfilled the custom of staying inside her house for a month of mourning. Relatives left, one by one. Mutombo returned to his family. Ngalula carried the news of Father's death back to our Christian people at Makala. I stayed with Mother to comfort her. When enough time had passed and everything was arranged, I brought Mother and her things to live with Ngalula and me at Makala.

When I returned to the city I discovered that the word dipanda had spread like a dry-season fire. It had opened wounds wider. People spoke words of hate which caused me fear.

People of our former masters' tribe were saying, "We are natives of this part of the country. We are more numerous than those of our slave tribe. We will rule here. If the slave tribesmen do not want to work under us, we will wage war against them and drive them out. Why should they continue to eat from our cooking pot? Let them go eat out of their own. Let them return to their fatherland where they came from."

Our tribesmen replied, "God heard the cry of Israel and delivered them from their Egyptian masters. He enabled them to spoil the Egyptians and led them to their fatherland. If it is thus with us, He will likewise hear our cry. He will deliver us. If He wants us to return to our fatherland, we will not go empty-handed. We will first spoil your wealth."

Words like these spoken to each other fanned the flames of hatred. These flames began to catch the people of God. Bit by bit, the church was cut into pieces like the carcass of an animal; the bones were chopped to bits, fixing it for the cooking pot. Among my Christians I noticed a few of both tribes who fought hard to guard the cords of love which had tied us as one.

Because of suspicions which grew and grew, the white man and the black man were split asunder. One day in the city I was surprised to see my friend of long ago, Mukosa. He had been in my class at Kombe. Now he was doing the work of an evangelist in villages of the headhunting tribe. He told me how people of that tribe were preparing for independence.

"As you know, Bula Matadi had never mentioned the word dipanda," he began. "Our people hunted everywhere to find out what it means."

"Have they found the answer?" I asked.

"Yes, when a cockroach appears, some chicken will be there to eat it. So when this hunger appeared, someone showed up who could finish it. His name was Buana. One day the village chief called everyone together and introduced this stranger. Because of his wisdom in strong medicines, he harmonized with the spirits, and they revealed to him a secret. As you know, our people have much faith in any message from our venerated departed ones."

"What was the secret?"

"He said the spirits were angry because the white man has refused to show us where his wealth comes from. In addition, the white man has squeezed from us more wealth;

144

he has forced us to pay taxes. So our ancestral spirits are tearing our land from the hands of the white man; they want to give it back to us."

"And will dipanda bring us the white man's wealth?" I asked.

"Oh, yes. Buana assured the village people that the white man's guns, his trucks, his clothing, his money, would soon be ours. But the spirits could not bring us these things until we carried out their commands. They said we must cleanse our country of pollution caused by the white man."

"What must the villagers do to cleanse themselves of this pollution?"

"Buana reminded them that they had spent all their time to make the white man happy. They had neglected to do things that make the spirits happy. He ordered them to clean weeds from the paths to the cemeteries. He told them to clean the grave sites. He told them that white things defile our country. Our people must get rid of their white chickens and white goats. He said pigs are filthy animals which defile the land; also the spirits are disturbed by their grunting. Pigs must be destroyed. On the day before dipanda comes, the villagers are to put large empty boxes on the grave sites. If they have carried out the instructions of the spirits well, the morning of the day of dipanda they will find the boxes filled with the things of the white man."

"And have the villagers done these things?"

"Oh, yes. I told them they were foolish for killing their animals. After dipanda comes, they will need them to eat. But they said the white man was paying me to say those things so they wouldn't get his wealth. They said I was trying to ruin what the spirits wanted to do for them. They threatened to drive me from the village. They said one rotten flying ant will spoil a basketful. So they ate as many of their animals as they could and sold the rest for nothing.

145

They have made new paths to the grave sites. They have gotten big boxes for themselves. Some of them expect to receive the white man's cars and trucks. They have even built bamboo shelters to keep them in. They are waiting, their hearts suspended, for the arrival of the day of dipanda."

"Did Buana stay to help them?"

"No. They paid him his fee of three pigs and two goats; then he went to carry his good news to other villages. These days there are many people declaring messages like Buana's. As the lead goat goes, so goes all who follow. Tribesmen in all our villages are following the teachings of these foolish leaders."

"Has Bula Matadi tried to help the village people understand what dipanda really is?"

"Yes, but it's too late. One afternoon six strange men came to the village. They were wearing high-priced clothing and were riding new bicycles. They were sent by Bula Matadi. They gathered the people and told them what dipanda will mean. They said African leaders will be over them. Laws will still be enforced. Taxes will still be paid. They must sit quietly in their villages; they must respect their leaders and work hard. Then some day our country would be great and rich; then everybody would be happy. When the men finished talking, they gave each person a little book written in the white man's language; its title was, 'What Is Independence?'"

"Did the village people accept the words of the visitors?"

"Not a bit. They said, 'The white man has hidden this affair from us all these years, why would he tell us the truth about it now? He is just working hard to continue hiding the secrets our forefathers have now revealed to us. It is true that black men brought us his message. But where did these messengers get their nice clothes and their new

146

bicycles? From the white man. He is paying them well. Why shouldn't they say what he tells them to say?' "

"What did they do with the little books?"

"They could not understand why the white man wanted them to hold in their hands paper leaves which they couldn't read. As you know, almost none of our village people have gone to school enough days to read the white man's language. They feared the paper leaves might be a kind of medicine the white man was using to curse them. They destroyed them."

"Has no one suspected that the words of Buana might be wrong?"

"One night, after the village people had already obeyed the laws of Buana, one of our tribal leaders spoke on my radio; he sits in the city of Kinshasa. Many of the village men came to my house and listened to him. His words were much like the words spoken by the men sent from Bula Matadi. Afterwards I heard our older men talking to each other. They said that if Buana, the seer, had deceived them—if he had caused them to destroy their animals for nothing—they would bite the seer in the eye. They would hunt down Buana and do to him as he had forced them to do to their animals. They swore among themselves to seal their curse upon him by cutting his body to pieces and burning it in the forest."

It was not only the headhunter tribe which was suspicious about the white man. Almost nobody would any longer believe what he said. Rather, as the headhunting people had done, they wanted to believe the opposite of what he said. Some people reminded us that new covenants are always sealed with a sacrifice shedding its blood. Thus on the day of dipanda, when the flag of our new country was raised, some people would be sacrificed; the blood of people would fall to the ground.

Others said the white man was angry because the black people were getting their independence. When that day came, he would send airplanes to drop bombs on their villages and destroy them. Others talked about Bula Matadi's plans to have all the village people gather at his house for a day of feasting and rejoicing on the day of dipanda. They said he wanted to gather all together so his soldiers could kill them all with guns. There was no one who knew what to believe. Every ear listened for something new; hearts began to tremble. And as the hearts of all people began to tremble, the earth began to tremble.

The day of dipanda came. People ran to the grave sites to look into the boxes. They found them empty. The village people were overwhelmed with wrath, with shame, with disappointment. Men like Buana disappeared at once.

Some people stayed inside their houses, closing the doors and windows, waiting in fear. Other people strengthened their hearts; they went to the feasts prepared by Bula Matadi. He raised the new flag. Nobody died. Then people who had come began to play, to dance, to drink, to rejoice. Bula Matadi gave his authority to Africans whom villagers had chosen but had not learned to respect. Then Bula Matadi said farewell and returned to his home country.

Bula Matadi had ruled with strong authority. Thus at this time, our country was as a heavy stone wall which had been built slowly through many years. But he had failed to teach others how to rule with strong authority. So when Bula Matadi left, we began to eat the fruits of his neglect.

Lies which people were telling each other to fill the emptiness, fears which made hearts tremble continually, passions of men to gain wealth quickly, were like winds, blowing everybody this way and that. Now these winds gathered themselves at one place and made a storm. This terrible storm made black clouds that covered our earth. It chased white men ahead of it. It left behind it pieces of people that would not fit together anymore—pieces of lust, of grief, of hate, of revenge, pieces that had once helped each other give the land quietness and order.

A snake cannot cut itself into pieces. Trouble requires people on two sides. Our tribes began to accuse each other of planning war. Men began carrying hunting guns, or spears, or bows and arrows. One tribe would send spies to villages of the other tribe, to learn if they were making plans for war. When tribesmen of these villages learned of the spies, they accused the other tribe of sending spies to plan attacking them. The earth trembled more and more. It shook. It split. War came out.

Cockroaches, to escape being killed, run around at night. Warriors did not come to trouble people during the light of day. It was in the darkness of night, when people were sleeping, that they crept slowly to a village. They encircled it. Then, when their leader gave them a sign, they put fire to the grass of the hut roofs. People woke up, flames falling upon them. They ran screaming from their huts. Warriors, waiting for them outside, shot them down as they fled. This happened here, then there, then at another place. Soon it was happening everywhere, as bits of fire scattered by the winds.

In such troubles, there was one person remaining among us who could perhaps help us. He had been with us when we sat in peace; he was now with us in our suffering. He might be able to keep our country from falling apart. He was the missionary.

The missionary threw himself into work as a good swimmer throws himself into a great river. He would pass hours sitting with village chiefs, talking of peace. When warriors began their journey to fight, he would go ahead of them with the Bible in hand, talk with them, and turn them back.

149

After a village raid, he would heal the burned and wounded. Thus where there was a missionary, people stopped quaking. They began breathing again. Truly, the mortar in the wall had crumbled badly, but because of the work of the missionary, the rocks still held together. The wall stood for today, for tomorrow, for the next day. Then came another storm.

Bitter seeds which had been planted in Father's heart when he was a child, which still remained in the hearts of those still living, began to sprout and bear fruit. The soldiers began to take vengeance on the white man. Now they could repay him.

As white men through all the past years had finished their lust by lying with black women, now the soldiers thus used white women. They struck the white men with their guns. They made them undress, except for a waist cover, and hoe weeds in the sun. They made white men dance while they shot at their feet. They threatened to kill them. But in other ways, the soldiers restrained their revenge; it was not fully an eye for an eye. We did not hear that they killed many white people, or cut off their hands, or crushed the heads of their babies.

Storm winds were spreading these affairs rapidly across the breadth of our country. The missionary who lived outside our city called for a meeting of the Christians. We went to the mission post and gathered in the church. My heart felt like a cloth, twisted tight, and dried by sadness.

"In times past, many Christians have died because they were followers of Jesus Christ," he said. "We Christians today should be willing to lay our lives onto the ground for our faith also. You know what soldiers are doing these days. Are they tormenting us because of our faith? No. They are troubling us because of the color of our skin.

"I think I am ready to die for my faith," he continued.

"But should I pay the price of my life because I have white skin? Shall I let soldiers do me or my wife badly because we have white skin? Is this a sacrifice which would make the church stronger? While we are among you, are we not drawing soldiers toward us as a cadaver draws animals who would eat it? If soldiers came, would they not cause you much suffering if you tried to protect us?

"It does not seem wise for us to stay with you at this time," he said. "If we remain alive, we will be able to return and help you again. We wish to go sit across the border south of here. We will wait there. We hope only a few weeks will pass until we see you again. We invite the pastor or some other strong Christian to move into our house and watch our things until we return."

The missionary was leaving. We were as people struck by lightning. We could not believe it. We wept. We wailed. No one wailed more than I. As our forefathers had always wailed for the loss of one they loved, as my relatives had wailed for the loss of Father, now I sat on the floor and wailed our loss. We feared that now the mortar holding the stones would turn into dust and the wall would collapse, letting our country fall apart.

❀ ❀ ❀

Everybody leans on the mortar. When it is taken away, all the village people suffer. There is no ground pepper for greens, no flour for bidia, no powerful pounded medicine to heal our sicknesses. Everyone mourns.

14

The missionary left. As he had requested, Ngalula, my mother and I brought our things onto the mission post. We moved into the missionary's house to take care of his things. But in time of war people are fleeing from death; they don't remember the laws of respecting the things of others. They say, "The owner of these things has gone forever. His things will help us save our lives. It is foolish not to use them." My tribemates knew I was now guarding such things. They came to me for help. I saw them in the path coming. I stood in the doorway to greet them.

"You are our blood relative," they said. "We expect your help if fighting comes."

"What do you want me to do to help you?" I asked.

"You have a tall strong body. You have a powerful foreign-made gun like few people have. Are you not also keeping the missionary's gun?"

"Do you see that it is the business of a pastor to fight against the flesh and blood of people?" I asked. "I have been teaching these people in the house of God. Now, how can I drain their blood onto the ground?"

"Do you think they really accepted the things you taught them in the house of God? If they had, would they be wanting to kill our wives and children now? Those things have no value now. We must join together to stay alive. We must prepare ourselves to fight."

"Do as you wish about preparing yourselves to fight. I am not starting to fight today. I have been fighting for many days. I have been fighting the authorities of darkness which make men hate each other. In fighting, I know only one gun. It is my Bible."

"What power does that gun have? Is it restraining others from wanting to kill us? The time has come for us to work with guns which make people fear. If you are afraid to cause blood-letting, then give us your gun; then you won't need to enter the fighting. We'll guard you, as well as our wives and children."

"God has made me a shepherd of the souls of all men," I said. "I could give you my gun, but when you break a twig, all the animals in the jungle hear it. The news would spread everywhere. After you defeated the other tribesmen, could I ever be a shepherd to them again?"

"Thus you think it is no affair for them to kill us? It is more important that they stay alive so that you could be the shepherd of *their* souls? Are you not our blood relative? Offend one goat for its long front teeth and you offend goats everywhere. Do you not have shame to so offend the tribe that gave birth to you? Thus you have renounced us. You refuse to give us your gun. Only give us the gun of the missionary. There is not a person who will recognize it."

"I could do as you wish and give you his gun," I replied. "But you would use it to kill people. Other people might not know. But I do not work for man; I work for God. He would know. He has given me the work of saving souls; He has not given me the work of destroying bodies. If I gave you the missionary's gun would not the blood of other people be on my hands? Would not this memory torture me? How could I be happy?"

"We know why you talk like that. It is because you have made friendship with our enemies. You want to betray us. You plan to give them the guns."

"It makes no difference who the person is or what tribe he

is from. I have one word for anyone who wants these guns. Let them kill me first. Then when I have fallen to the ground, let them climb up over my body and take them."

"Then if you shake your responsibility to help us from your hands, we shake from our hands responsibility to protect you or those you love," they said. "When trouble catches you and your crying reaches up to heaven, don't hunt for us. Your trouble will be your affair."

They walked away, the fire of anger in their legs. After they had gone, I hid the guns between the ceiling and the roof. Thus if they burned the house the guns would be destroyed.

I knew it would be thus: the animals of the jungle hear the breaking of the twig. Word spread rapidly that I had refused to let my tribemates have the guns. This showed people of other tribes that I did not have partiality. It showed them that I loved everybody. I refused fighting. I was a man of peace. Thus I walked around among all kinds of people without trouble. Everyone welcomed me. When I taught them of Jesus Christ, their hearts drank my words as if they were medicine which healed people's souls.

I began to see that I had taken the place of the missionary. As our people in trouble had leaned upon him for strength, now they leaned upon me. If strong Christians all across our country were working as hard as I was, perhaps we could keep the wall from falling. Perhaps we could keep the pieces of our country together.

Then a journey caught me—a journey to a marriage. I was not home for three nights. A proverb says that the gourd bringing water from the spring does not break until it is close to the cooking pot in the kitchen. Thus when it appeared that people might sit quietly in peace and our country might progress bit by bit, something happened. So the gourd, filled with our hopes, fell to the ground and broke into pieces. When I returned, Ngalula told me what had happened.

"On the morning of the third day," she began, "when I went out of the house, I saw that during the night someone had painted this red X on our door."

This was our custom in time of fighting, to show that a house is to be destroyed and that those living in it are to be killed.

"Someone wants to take the guns by force," I reasoned. "But as our custom is to start fighting at night, my heart was not troubled until darkness came. I did not light the lamps. Mother and I sat waiting, listening. The darkness was black—as charcoal. Mother wanted to begin death mourning; I quieted her. I did not want anyone outside to hear us.

"In the middle of the night," Ngalula continued, "before the first cock crowed, I heard noise like footsteps outside. Now our affair is finished, I told myself. More time of quietness passed. All at once, I heard a gun shot. It was on the hillside below our house. Men cried out and there were more gun shots. Then I heard men running past our house toward the fighting. I listened closely to know who they were. I heard them talking as they passed. They were our tribemates going to help those fighting. They drove the attackers down the hill. Then we waited again in quietness, until morning came."

"Do you truly know that those who chased away the attackers were our tribemates?" I asked Ngalula.

"Yes. They talked as our people talk."

"Do you think our tribemates would come to protect the lives of you and Mother? I doubt it. They have already pushed this burden off their hands. But they would not want the guns to fall into the hands of their enemies. It appears that warriors of our former masters' tribe marked our house to be attacked so they could get the guns.

Warriors of our tribe heard about it; they came here to wait for them. When warriors of our masters' tribe came to finish their plan, our warriors chased them away."

That afternoon a large group of my tribemates came to see me. All of them were carrying spears or jungle knives or guns.

"Did you hear what happened while you were gone?" they said. "We saved the lives of your wife and mother."

I knew what they said was true.

"What if you had been home and we had not come? Would you have chased them away with your Bible? Or would you have used your gun?"

"I am grateful to God for ways He arranges to spare the lives of His children," I said. "Even if I had been here, it would have been useless for me to use my gun. I, one person, could not have driven them away. When the time comes which God has written for us to die, guns will make no difference. We will be ready to die."

"So it would have been better for us to let them kill your wife and mother and burn down your house?"

"You decided in your hearts to come protect my loved ones and my things. Ngalula and Mother are still alive. For this I am grateful."

"Look," said one. "Clear up to this time, he is still living with one foot in the mortar and one foot in the cooking pot, as is his custom."

"What will you do for us to show your thanks?" they asked.

"What do you want me to do for you?" I asked.

After a pause, another spoke angrily.

"Stop trying to sidestep this way and that with words. Are we little children? Haven't you heard that they attacked and burned a village of our clansmen up the road last night? They held the young chief on the ground and cut off his

156

head. His body stood and ran before it stumbled, like a chicken with its head cut off. They tried to massacre his family. They hacked his baby to death with a jungle knife and threw the meat of it against a tree. We are in war. We have fought to save the lives of your loved ones. We have come to demand that you join us in fighting to save the lives of our loved ones. This is what we want."

This news hit me like a bolt of lightning. I wondered if it were rumor or truth. It would not do to ask them.

"Look," I said, stretching my hands out in front of me. "These hands have healed you in sickness. They have comforted you in sorrow. These hands have baptized many of you. They have dedicated your babies. It is not right for them to spill human blood onto the ground. I am not a politician. I am not a soldier. In all the days which are past, I have been your pastor. Accept for me to still be simply your pastor."

"We have not come for nothing," they replied. "We have been sent with a commission. The chief sent us to get those guns. For this reason there are forty of us. If you refuse to give them to us, we will take them by force."

"I am not strong enough to fight all of you," I replied. "But I will resist until death for anyone to get those guns. If you kill me, there will be no one left to care for my wife and mother; you should kill them too. But after you have killed us, I doubt if you will find the guns. I've hidden them so they cannot be found."

The warriors began arguing among themselves.

"He refuses to fight," said some. "He refuses to give us the guns. Because of this, some of our tribemates will die. He is no better than those who are killing us. Let's finish him."

"Why should we kill him if afterwards we will not be able to find the guns?" said others. "Let us accept his words that he will fight for nobody."

"He is lying. Can't you see he has married another wife? He's eating out of the hand of a stranger. If you follow this wisdom, you will find his guns in the hands of our enemies, butchering us. If he had hid the guns so well, we should kill him to make sure the enemy will not get them."

"You can do with me what you like," I said. "But if I live or die, I assure you that no one will use the guns in battle."

When they wearied themselves arguing, they began to offend me. "What contemptuous disrespect you have for the lives of your tribemates," they said. "We desert you. We no longer count you a blood brother. Because you are of our tribe, the enemy will not protect you. The husband of many wives habitually goes to bed hungry. There is no person who cares for you. We are going to battle. We warn you now. You had better flee. If there is great bloodshed—if any of our loved ones are slain—when the war is finished, we will return to take vengeance on you and those you love."

When darkness came we gave ourselves into the hands of God and went to bed. But we could not sleep. In the middle of the night the red glow of fire shone through a window onto the walls of our room. Then there was shooting and screaming. I rose to look. War had broken out in the village just off the mission post. Huts had been changed into ovens, their roofs sending flames high into the sky. People ran here and there as crazy. Screaming women, holding their babies, dragging their children, fled from among the burning houses toward the darkness.

Two men held a third man on the gound; they worked over him with fury. Then a gun sounded. One man fell, the other rose and fled, but the man on the ground did not move. Other men stood fighting each other with the rage of crazy animals. I knew what they were holding in their hands: jungle knives, bicycle chains, broken bottles. As I

158

watched them striking one another, I could feel the pain in my own body.

Ngalula and I knelt by the bed to pray. We cried out to God, weeping. We prayed until the noises of fighting ceased. Then we sat and waited for morning.

We did not know what would happen that day. Before last night, men had plotted evil against us to get the guns. One tribe had marked us to be killed; the red X was still on our door. The other tribe had threatened to come and take the guns by force. And since last night's occurrence their rage and hatred for each other would be as hot as fire. Now nothing would restrain them from doing whatever they felt they needed to do in order to strengthen themselves for the bigger fighting ahead. I knew that if they came for the guns now, we could trust only the mercy of God.

But no one came that day. Perhaps they were caring for their wounded and burying their dead; perhaps they were waiting for the night when they could come, no one seeing them.

Our trouble was great. We wished it would stay light forever. But the sun set as on all other days. When darkness came, we sat and waited. Mother knew this might be our last night on earth. She would start quietly mourning our death wail; we would silence her and comfort her with words from the Bible. We prayed. The night passed slowly, as a whole year of darkness. Our bodies became weak as tattered cloths on a washing stone. Then suddenly, in the middle of the night, there was a knock on the door.

I did not answer at first. I knew my answering might be the beginning of our dying. But I knew also that if we did not answer, they would break the door. When they found us, they would be angrier. I went to the door. Making my voice calm I said, "Yes?"

"Pastor, is that you?"

"Yes. Who are you?"

"This is your brother in Jesus, David Kalala. I wish to have a word with you. Let me in."

Kalala was an elder in my church. He was of our former masters' tribe—the tribe with which we were at war.

"Are others with you?"

"I am alone."

I remembered Kalala was one who had tried hard to keep us tied together as Christians. I decided to believe him. I opened the door; he entered and I closed it behind him.

"War between our tribes is spreading. My clansmen have evil plans. It is not safe for you to stay here. I left my truck down the road. Another brother is guarding it. I did not want its noise to arouse suspicion. You must get together the things you want to take with you. I will come with the truck in half an hour. We will load it and leave hurriedly, before they come looking for you."

Could this be part of a plot to deliver me into the hands of Kalala's tribemates? Was this a clever plan to get us out of the house so they could come and ransack it to find the guns? Could I trust myself, Ngalula and Mother into the hands of Kalala? Could Christian love cause a person to risk being killed by his own people in order to save me? Then I realized that it was the same way between my people and me. Because of my love for others, I had risked being killed by them. This is how God turns peoples' hearts around when they love Him. Kalala's face seemed to show me he was speaking the truth. I decided to trust him.

"Where will you take us?" I asked.

"If you are wise, you will let me take you to your home country. Then I know you will be safe."

"But that is far. It takes us through the country where only your tribemates live. We will not be able to arrive tonight. We will have to travel also during the light of day tomorrow. If your tribemates caught you trying to escape with us, they might kill you."

"I know my tribemates. If you stay here, you will die. If you leave with me, you may escape. We do not want to stop in the road; people will find us and ask questions. We have poured the gas tanks full. We will drive until we arrive. Our time is short. Get your things together. I will be back soon."

I began to feel sure that God had sent His angel to deliver us. Ngalula and I began to gather our things together. We prodded Mother to stop her mourning and help us. Kalala's truck was small. We could not take all our things. We had worked hard for many years to accumulate them. They were a symbol of progress. They were important. What we left, we would never see again. But our elders say, in trouble, the big thing is to have a head on your neck; wealth is nothing. Things could be replaced. Our lives could not. We forced ourselves to choose what to take, and what to leave.

We would take the things which had cost the most— things which it would not be easy for us to buy again. Wherever we went, it should be easy to replace common things.

So in a box we packed our nicest eating dishes and cooking dishes, wrapping them in our nicest clothing. I hid all the money we had in the pockets of trousers and coats. We folded our blankets and sheets and our one nice bedspread. We would take our mattress. There would not be room for the bed frame.

We would take two drums of manioc flour and one of corn flour. This would feed us until we found a place to live and could buy other food. What about my animals? I would take two she-goats and one he-goat. I would take one basket filled with hens and one rooster. The rest would remain.

What about my mill? It would help me very much in

making a living. But there would not be room enough for it. And the guns. One of them would be very helpful to kill meat for food. While I was thinking of them, I heard the truck arriving. There would not be time to take the guns from their hiding place. They would stay.

Kalala had backed his small truck to our door. We put things into it until it was full, and left, driving without lights. David, his friend and Ngalula sat in front. Mother and I sat among the things in the rear. We drove on and on, through many villages which were silent and dark. We knew that inside those huts were men waiting with weapons. As they feared the truck might be bringing a load of warriors to attack them, they remained silent. As we were afraid of being discovered, we kept going.

We did not stop until light of morning began to show in the east. Then when we were passing through a village, I heard noise like the shot of a gun. The truck jerked to one side and stopped. I could see no one. The village was quiet.

Kalala opened the door quietly and said, "A front tire split; we must put on another one."

"Is the other one strong?" I asked.

"Yes, it is good. But I have nothing with which to raise the truck. Come and see if we can lift it."

Because we could not bring the mill, we had brought the wooden mortar in which Ngalula pounded flour. Quietly and hurriedly, we three men lifted the front of the truck. Ngalula placed the mortar beneath it. We prayed God would keep the villagers asleep or inside their huts. We saw no one. We changed the tire and continued on our journey.

We traveled into the hours of daylight, finally reaching the big city of Malandi. Here lived David Tshisanga, my old friend, who first taught me to love Jesus long ago. But this was not the time for hunting friends. It was time for journeying. Many soldiers were here, so people sat quietly. We bought gasoline and continued.

This country was strange to me. Tribes were not mixed up here. All these villages were of Kalala's tribe; thus only news of war had reached them. People sat outside their huts and watched us, questions on their faces. I tried to sit low among our things. We did not wave. We kept going. Toward the middle of morning, the truck began to slow down. I arose slowly to look ahead of us. A large pole lay across the road. Men were standing by it. The road was blocked.

We came to the pole and stopped. Two of the four men came to the truck. One had a gun; the others had jungle knives.

"Life to you, tribemates!" Kalala said with happiness.

They did not return the greeting. The one with the gun spoke.

"They have placed us here to know who passes up and down the road," he said. "You are approaching the borderline which separates us from the land of our slave tribe. They stirred up the people to ask for dipanda; now they are stirring up people to war. We are to see that you are carrying no such troublemakers or their weapons."

"We have come from Makala," Kalala replied. "Trouble is there too. But all of us do not want war. This is a pastor who would not get mixed up in the fighting. I am taking him and his family to the borderline; then I will return."

"Let us see his papers."

I showed him my tax book and the mission card showing I was a pastor. In them he read the name of my home country and the name of my tribe.

"You get down out of the truck," he ordered me.

With much fear I got out of the truck.

"Stand over there," he said, pointing to one side.

"We do not know," he said to Kalala. "Maybe you are lying. You could be a traitor to your tribe. You may be trying to escape with this man. You could be carrying guns to his people."

"To know I am telling you the truth, look through the things I am hauling. If you find a gun, then you will know that I am a liar; then you can take us all captive and do what you want with us."

My heart leaped as I remembered how I had almost brought a gun. God had restrained me. They began opening boxes and stirring up our things. I did not care for things now. They could keep them all if they desired. All I prayed for was our lives.

They finished searching and left the box lids half closed on our mixed-up things.

"This man has many things," the man with the gun said. "He must be someone important."

"He is important," Kalala said. "He is my pastor. He taught me of Jesus. For years he has taught many of our tribemates and others about Jesus. When men hated each other and were talking of war, this man's teaching was like medicine that kept them from fighting. When I saw this I decided that men like him should not die. They should live forever. If there were many in our country like him men would not be killing each other, they would be living in peace. Thus if someone must die, let it be me; I am not as important as he is."

The men were quiet for a time. Then the leader said, "People who pass through our barrier pay us a price for our help. What will you give us?"

"We are happy for your help," Kalala said. "We would not accept it for nothing. Here, take these goats and chickens."

Two of the men took them out of the truck; the other two

moved the pole barrier to one side. I got into the truck, Kalala started the motor, waved at the men and drove off.

We stopped at the first village across the tribal border. I could tell at once that I was among people of my own tribe. They came cautiously to the truck. I met them and explained who I was. They rejoiced and shook both my hands vigorously. We unloaded our things. Then I turned to say good-by to Kalala.

I held his hand in both of mine.

"In olden days, God sent an angel to close the mouths of lions to deliver Daniel," I said. "Today God has done the same for me. What will I ever pay you, my brother?"

"When God rewards His people, He will pay me. I must return. There are others I may be able to help."

We embraced each other, weeping like little children. Then he let go of me, got into his truck, turned it around and drove off toward the men with the pole across the road.

The women took Ngalula and Mother to where they could rest. Then we found places for our things, dividing them between different village huts. Then I sat on a chair to rest—to pick up the pieces of my mind and put them together—to talk over all of these things with God.

I praised Him for delivering us. He had shown me clearly that my Bible was a gun with power—with more power than a gun of wood and iron. After independence, when hatred and suspicion began splitting the church into pieces, it looked as if my teaching had been wiped out. But it had not. It had borne fruit. It had given us Kalala, to whom we owed the debt of our lives. I knew that there were many other men like Kalala.

It was clear that what was going on at Makala was a little picture of what was going on in larger cities all across our country. Greed and jealousy were splitting the tribes. War was being provoked. Our people were fleeing to stay alive. Among them were those I loved.

There was Mutombo and his large family at Lusama to the north and Ndaya, my sister, who lived at the city of Lubumbashi far to the southeast. What was happening to them? I prayed for them. I asked God to help them find angels of mercy, like my friend Kalala.

✿　✿　✿

It is better to sleep with an empty stomach than with a troubled heart.

15

I woke up early the next morning. There was much to do.
First I wanted to see if Ngalula and Mother had rested
well. Mother was getting old. The last days at Makala and
the long trip had tired her. I wondered if she understood
that we had escaped only because God had done for us an
amazing thing. Also, I must find a truck which would move
our things clear into the middle of our country, away from
the border with other tribes. We wanted to build our home
where the sufferings of war would not trouble us again.

Ngalula's smile told me that her heart was at peace. I
found Mother in the hut where she had slept. She was
squatting by a small fire which someone had started in the
center of the floor.

"Did you sleep well?" I asked.

"I slept well."

"Does your body still have strength?"

"I am weary because of the journey, but it is no affair."

"How do you feel about the affairs of these last few
days?"

"We were dead people," she said. "Then Mvidi Mukulu
did a surprising thing. He saved us by the hands of a man
who could have killed us. One of the hunters took us out of
the trap which had caught us. Mvidi Mukulu saw that the
time was not yet sufficient for us to die."

"Mother, having seen these things with your eyes, how do
you feel about the affair of Jesus?"

"My watching the affair of Jesus did not begin with these

troubles. It began long ago when the white man gave **Ndaya** medicine which saved her life. I could not say much while your father was with us; his heart was bad toward the white man. But I kept the affair of Ndaya and other affairs like it in my heart. All these years I have watched your walking. I heard the words you spoke to those who wanted to kill you. Then when I saw that death was near, I began to mourn. But I heard the prayers of you and Ngalula. Mvidi Mukulu heard your pleading and did something no person would expect. All these things have shown me clearly that the affairs you teach are true."

"So you have accepted in your heart the affair of Jesus?"

"How could I refuse? He delivered us. He is stronger than the things we have been putting our faith in. I do not yet understand Him well. But I have accepted Him. My ears are open. I will listen well to your teaching. I will learn."

The tiny bird which few people see has eyes which see in the darkness. Mother had seen through her darkness. I bowed my head and prayed with her. I told Jesus of my joy that Mother had opened her heart to Him. I went and told Ngalula. My burden had lightened. The days ahead would be easier. Mother was prepared to die.

I found a tribemate with a truck. The next day he carried us and our things to the midst of the land of our ancestors. Then I saw with my own eyes the picture Father had painted when he spoke to us many years ago. Here were the great open grassy plains, rolling gently like waves blown by a soft wind. From time to time we saw deeper valleys, where belts of jungle followed twisting streams. Once we crossed a rushing river. Upstream I saw a great wall of stone rising up from the river's edge. Away from the river, the wall became lost in a hill that was covered over with forest. I looked hard at the wall, to see if there were any caves. It was good to be here in this quiet country, whose earth had heard the steps of our ancestors. But as our fathers say, it is the quiet tepid water that drowns the most people. Though I did not know it now, this quiet country would swallow many of us.

We chose to sit at a village called Kamuanga, where three roads meet. At first it had been a small village, but now many tribemates, chased away from their homes in many distant places, were coming here to live. There was no longer place to build houses along the roads; hundreds of new huts were appearing on the hillsides around us. This would be a good place to stay. Here would be many sheep waiting for a shepherd.

In the weeks that followed our bodies became weary from work we had not done for many years. With our hands we built ourselves a house, carrying sticks and cut grass and packed mud. I remembered how we had despised such a house at Makala when we moved into our brick one. Had not those thoughts been foolish? This house we had built with our own hands, and was it not nice? We were proud of it. We were content.

We cleared ground with our hoes and planted a garden. Every day Ngalula and Mother carried our water from the stream. We could not buy meat; everyone wanted to keep his animals for breeding. We could not hunt fish like our ancestors had; we had lost the art. Some of us made bows, arrows and spears and tried to learn how to hunt with them again. From time to time a trader would bring a truck full of dried fish. We remembered when we had despised it. Now people fought with each other to buy it.

All food had hard prices, because there was so little of it. Our money began to disappear rapidly. We began to spend it very carefully. The nice things we had brought with us did little to help us. The dishes stayed in the box—these were not days to feed guests on pretty dishes, these were days when every man measured out his food, ate alone and wondered about the days that were coming.

Meat had disappeared; we ate only bidia and cooked greens. We knew the flour we had brought with us would not last forever. It would be more than a year before the manioc in our garden would be ready to eat. We would have to trust the forest and stream and the ground beneath our feet to feed us. If these failed, we would sit in hunger. But these were only the beginnings of our sufferings. As a goat cannot refuse its tether, so we could not refuse the troubles which dipanda had tied us with.

Meanwhile every day trucks arrived filled full of people who had fled from here and there, bringing with them the few things they could carry. Whenever I heard a truck had arrived from the direction of Lusama or Lubumbashi, I would go rapidly to where they were unloading. I would search among the faces to find one I knew. Then I would return to my house, disappointed and wondering.

One afternoon when the sun was lowering I was watching another truck, its people and things pouring onto the ground. I waited until the last person had gotten out. All faces had been strange. As I started to walk to my house, I heard a voice of surprise call, "Mulumba!"

I turned and saw a woman as tall as I. She was coming toward me, her arms outstretched. Could this be—no. Not truly. She was too thin, and she looked old and tired. This could not be she. As she came closer, I saw her eyes. Then I knew. I grabbed her in my arms.

"Oh, Ndaya, our loved one—"

She sobbed and shook as she held me. Then her husband Leta and their four children arrived. They were alive! Joy! Joy that stuck out of the top of heaven and reached clear down to earth! Joy that left our bodies weak so that we could not stand. After resting, we walked to the house, and

Ndaya saw Mother again. Then we sat and looked at each other as dreamers, too weak with surprise and happiness to speak.

Only Ngalula remained with strength. She didn't measure the flour that night. When guests appear, something to feed them appears. She made the pot full. We ate bidia and greens; we ate abundantly. That night was not the fitting time to ask Ndaya and Leta of what had happened. They awoke late the next morning; then Leta told us their story.

"As you know, I had a good job in an office," he began. "When dipanda came, the local tribesmen who had remained behind us in many things became jealous. They wanted to chase away foreign tribesmen so they could have their jobs. I received letters threatening me, but I strengthened my heart and kept doing my work well.

"Some of my Christian friends were of the local tribe. They tried to help us. One afternoon one of my friends sent me a note in secret telling me that he had just learned that his tribemates were planning to force themselves into my house that night and kill me and my wife and children. He told me to try to get out before they arrived.

"When I got home I told Ndaya. She said, 'Where shall we flee to? It is already getting dark. You know how bad people wander in the streets at night. What would they do if they caught us foreign tribesmen and our children in the darkness? Also, how could we take any of our things with us? Let us give ourselves to God in prayer. If we die, let us die in our home.'

"Ndaya's faith was stronger than mine. But what else could we do? We said prayers with the children and put them to bed early. Then we turned out the lights, and sat on chairs on our front veranda, waiting. I held an empty bottle

171

in my hand. I told myself that I would hit one of them hard before they killed us.

"Ndaya sat up with me in the darkness until midnight had passed. Then she went to bed. A short time passed. Then I saw something in the road, moving close to the ground, slowly approaching our house. Looking closely, I came to understand that it was men with spears and knives, crawling on their stomachs. They moved a bit, very quietly, and stopped as if they were listening. Then they came closer. They entered our yard, always crawling on their bellies. I gripped my bottle hard; this was the time. But no! They were not coming up onto the veranda. They had stopped again and were listening as if they were afraid of something. I sat quiet as a dead man, watching. Then they began to crawl toward the back side of our house, always on their stomachs. Slowly, they went all around the house; they lay in the front yard listening for a short time. Finally they crawled out to the road and left as they had come. They returned and did the same thing two more times before daybreak.

"That day I went to work like on any other day," Leta continued. "Ndaya went to the market for food. Women of the local tribe met her there and asked her, 'What big affair was going on at your house last night?'

" 'There was nothing going on at our house last night,' she said.

" 'Oh, yes, there was,' they said. 'Our men came to see you. They said the house had lights everywhere. They saw people sitting in the windows and from inside the house came music and the noise of many people, as if you were having a big party. They said it continued all night long.'

"Ndaya did not reply. She knew that God had made them hear and see things which were not. Thus God had answered our prayers; He had saved our lives.

"Our seeing dipanda was like the weak man seeing the elephant; when he looked at it from far off, he wanted it; when he saw it close up, he fled from it. Because of the troubles of dipanda, soldiers of many countries had come to keep peace in our city. They were called "soldiers of the United Nations." They had cleaned off a big space outside the city where people whose lives were being threatened could come to live. We knew we could not expect to live if we stayed in our house, so we chose what things we could carry and fled to the camping space outside the city where we would be protected.

"We did not know it, but we were about to enter suffering we did not know was anywhere under the sun. Day following day, hundreds of our tribemates fled to the foreign soldiers for protection, until we were forty thousand people living one person on top of another. We could not sit with our children under the open sky. We sought to make ourselves a little house that would protect us from the rain and the hot sun and the cold at night.

"People made shelter places from whatever they could find. They made frames of weak sticks. Onto these frames they tied pieces of canvas, or old sacks, or cloth, or cardboard, or grass. But many others wandered around uselessly from here to there during the day, and when night came lay on the ground looking at the sky until the sun rose. But our troubles became greater.

"Bad people who had escaped from prisons came to the foreign soldiers to be protected too. The soldiers could not tell bad people from good people; they accepted everybody. At night, while people lay in their flimsy shelters or outside on the ground, they were robbed of the few things they had left. If they struggled, fighting broke out and they were wounded or killed. There was no night when people did not

173

die. We began burying the dead to one side of the camping space.

"While robbers tormented us at night, hunger and thirst tormented us by day. There was no water for washing our bodies. Often there was no water to drink. Children cried helplessly. We sat, parched on our insides from our mouths to our stomachs.

"Some of our tribemates were traders. They risked their lives to get food. They would slip out with their trucks at night and buy any food they could find. They would sell it to those of us who had money. The foreign soldiers would bring food during the day, but it was as nothing. People fought over it until it was finished. Many of the poor and weak people died from hunger. Others of us were eating as God feeds the birds that fly around in the sky. Others stayed alive by eating bits of food they begged off those who still had hearts of love.

"On top of this trouble, war caught us. Bullets were ripping through our cloth and cardboard houses like grains of corn thrown to chickens. What troubles, Brother! Where could we hide? Bullets killed men, women and little children.

"You know how men will hunt anything that might protect them when they are in such trouble. Our tribemates began making different kinds of fetishes which they said would protect us from death. Making and selling such useless things was their clever way of getting money to buy food. Many of those who had bought ancestral medicines died; we saw them. They died from either bullets, or hunger, or sickness. We could not leave the dead to rot under the open sun. We had to keep burying them. Someone was always busy digging holes for burying people. One day we stopped working to count graves. There were more than nine hundred.

174

"While many others bought medicines to protect themselves, a few of us fixed a little place to worship God. While people kept dying, we kept on fasting and praying, saying, 'The Lord is our Shepherd; we need nothing else.' God had mercy on us. He sent someone to help us.

"One day while we were worshiping, we saw that a white man had arrived. No other white man had dared entering our camping space without a gun. This man came empty-handed. Some of our men began speaking to him in our native tongue. They brought him to where we were worshiping.

" 'I am Preacher Lutongo,' he said. 'I sit in your home country.'

" 'Teach us from the Word of God,' we begged. 'We have not heard such words in many days.'

"He preached, his words falling as drops of water on parched and panting tongues.

"When he finished he said, 'I have come to see you in your suffering; I have come to hunt a way to help you.'

"Some of our tribemates said, 'He is lying. He is a spy sent to learn more about how we sit here. What he learns he will tell the soldiers so they can make more war on us. We should kill him.' Others said, 'A liar cannot thus speak the words of God. This man is speaking the truth. Let's trust him; perhaps he can help us.' Bit by bit, people began to trust his words.

"Lutongo arranged a special train to take all who wanted to leave. It had room for one thousand of us at a time. It would take two days to go and return. We would be traveling through country where there was war. In front of the engine were two flatcars. On each of them was piled a hill of sand bags. These heavy cars were to keep the engine from being thrown off the track if it were bombed. Behind the engine was a car with soldiers and big guns, sitting

175

behind walls of heavy iron. In the center of the train was another car with soldiers and big guns, and there was another at the end of the train.

"When the day arrived for us to leave we could not believe it was true. Lutongo was there to say farewell to us. We all sang, 'May God stay with you until we meet each other again,' and the train began its journey. Because of Lutongo's help, everybody left that place of suffering. Only the dead remained in their graves. The train took all of us to the town of Kamona. There big planes picked us up and brought us here to our home country.

"All these troubles have taught me, Brother, that God is worthy to be worshiped in whatever kind of affairs we find ourselves. We should look nowhere else. Only He alone has power to protect us in any kind of trouble under the sun which catches us."

✿ ✿ ✿

Night cannot stay forever; daybreak is coming.

176

16

Truly, God sends angels to take care of His children. The lives of Ndaya, Leta and their children had been spared, spared by miracles which followed one after the other. Those had been terrible days. But now they remained behind us. Ndaya and Leta sat with us, happy, rejoicing. Their youngest child, too small to walk, sat on the ground drawing child-pictures with her finger in the dust; the older children, all boys, played hide-and-hunt around the hut; they acted as if they'd had no troubles.

Their days of darkness at Lubumbashi were finished, but their troubles were not. An enemy which had caused the torment of death little by little there, had begun to work among us here. Each day he grew stronger. He became a master without love. His name was Hunger.

Every day more tribemates came. Many came as Leta, chased away from their homes by threats or violence. Many came because they heard of the homegoing of our tribes-people and they wanted to help build a great new tribal kingdom in the land of their forefathers. Almost all of them had lost their wealth and possessions. They came poor. They came in every path that ended here. Their number was as stones of gravel or as blades of grass—a many-ness too great to be counted. All were descendants of slaves who had become stronger than their masters. Now they entered a slavery of a different kind as they worked like slaves to stay alive.

One cannot cut dried skin with an eyelash; neither could

we cut a path of happiness through our troubles with so little in our hands. Everyone was in the same trouble. We ate less and less each day, fearing the day the flour would be finished. When that day came, we began to eat what grains we had reserved for seed. This left us nothing to plant. We would have to fight to stay alive the many months until manioc and corn in the new gardens could be harvested. Meanwhile, people kept coming. How would they stay alive? Would we sit alongside them and watch them die? Would we who were Christians share our gardens with the hungry? Would our few gardens deliver any of us from death, we being the many-ness of grasshoppers?

When our flour and seeds were finished, we began to eat like chickens, scratching and hunting for little things all of our waking hours. Children were left at home alone, older ones caring for the younger. Fathers and mothers would follow different paths with baskets or large basins. From dawn to darkness we would hunt for things to reduce our hunger. We hunted in forests for fruits and berries one could eat; we dug the ground searching for soft roots; we bought small portions of rice and manioc flour at terribly hard prices from traders who passed us. What we brought home we hid well inside our houses, lest someone crazy with hunger come and steal it.

But though we searched and searched, hunger grew. Our wailings, as one voice, reached up to high heaven:

> Our Mvidi Mukulu,
> Creator of all things,
> As people with itching sores who have no fingernails,
> We have teeth, but no food.
> Why did you give us strong teeth to eat with,
> And now fail to give us something to eat?

Hunger brought diseases we had never seen. It wasted the bodies of old people who were weak and of little children who nursed and nursed on breasts which were always empty.

The old people would try to endure the hunger pains without complaining, but the children would cry. For the first few days, a hungry child's cry is strong, his heart rebelling. Then slowly it becomes weak and begging. Then hunger stops causing pain and makes the body into a different thing. The arms become like straight black sticks, the joints like swollen knots. The chest becomes flat, the bones showing, and the stomach sticks far forward, like the bottom part of a drop of water. The child's hair bit by bit turns from black to yellow and then to white. Its eyes look out stiffly from deep dark holes. More and more, we saw white-haired children and white-haired old people sitting or lying on the ground, making no noise, looking hard at nothing. More and more fresh graves appeared between the huts.

Ngalula and I had never ceased wanting a child. But now we saw how children suffered. For this time of trouble we were content to be childless. We had more time to help others. When we were not hunting food, we tried to remind people of Jesus. No one ever suffered as He did. We knew that He was the only one who could heal hearts even in such suffering.

We tried to gather people into meetings to worship and pray, but people did not come. All their time, all the strength of their bodies, was given to the one work of fighting hunger. Those who were not out searching for food were sitting alongside their sick ones or burying their dead. In such trouble there is nothing as important as food. Something to wear is nothing; something to eat is everything. Lose your loincloth and your journey stumbles; lose your food and you die.

Though people did not have time to gather at one place for worship, I was sure they had not forgotten God. I knew

179

many people were crying to God from the mats where they lay, or from the gravesides of those just buried, or from secret prayer places to one side of the footpaths in the high grass. Ngalula, Mother and I had worship every day in our house. Mother's heart had been open to learn, but there had been no meat and little bidia for many days. Before our eyes, we watched her body weaken.

Our suffering would have been lightened a bit if we could have had other things to help us. But now, buildings which had been stores were empty shells. Everything had been sold. Small hospitals which had done much to heal sickness of village people in past years were also empty; their medicines were finished. Because there was no new cloth to be bought, people's clothing became ragged, their blankets became old. If the blankets were not washed they gathered vermin; if they were washed they fell into tatters, and people had nothing else to protect themselves from the cold at night.

Ngalula's dresses became so ragged they did not cover her body well. My clothing likewise wore out. We went through the boxes of nice things we had brought from Makala. We had no place else to go. We wondered how clothing could be so beautiful and we had thought it was as nothing. It was shame to wear such rich clothing now when everyone was in such terrible need. But it would have been more shameful to be naked. Ngalula chose a colorful wax blouse and wore it with her ragged skirt, and I began wearing my black suit trousers with my worn-out shirt.

If I could have used my bicycle, I could have gone on long journeys hunting for food or medicine. Though I always felt hunger, I still had strength of body to ride my bicycle. I could have gathered together a few things to comfort the most ill. But my bicycle had broken down long ago. No one knew where spare parts could be found. Thus I

180

had tied my bicycle frame beneath the roof of our house above our bedroom ceiling; by now it was covered with the dust of many days.

But in truth, trying to find enough things to restrain this much suffering was wasting time uselessly. The little food or medicine I might find after searching all day would help only a few people stay alive a little longer. Where could anyone find enough things to stop this much suffering? Such a quantity of things did not exist. I strengthened my heart to live with the suffering people and decided to feed the souls of those yet alive.

Therefore I no longer tried to gather people for worship. I began visiting them in their homes. I tried to find old people whose bodies showed they were suffering from hunger, but whose minds were yet clear. I sang songs and prayed with them, to help them forget about hunger. I tried to persuade them to open their hearts to Jesus Christ; then if death came, they could leave this earth in peace.

I learned to recognize homes where death would be coming. Thus I watched the coming of death to the youngest child of Ndaya and Leta, their only girl. For many days she had not sat on the ground drawing pictures with her finger in the dust. Hunger, without mercy, had changed her body. She lay on a mat quietly, looking hard at nothing, waiting forever for nothing.

Because of our marriage customs, at least one girl among boys is very important. After God had spared their lives through the Lubumbashi troubles, Leta was sure God would bring them all alive through the present time of trouble. "Could we be as flying ants, who struggle to escape from a hole in the ground only to be eaten?" he asked. But the little girl died. Though her parents spoke nothing, their faces showed that sorrow had torn their hearts into helpless little pieces.

I tried to be present where death had come. Among those who had come from far places were older people who had no one to care for them. There were also orphans, sometimes sisters and brothers, their parents having been killed in tribal fighting. People fought to keep their own children alive; they had nothing to give to outsiders. Thus these old people and children wandered, begging. They died sooner than others. We would find their bodies lying along a road or footpath. I helped bury them.

Ngalula and I did all we could for Mother. We watched helplessly as the signs of her hunger disease grew from day to day. We knew that unless we found help for her, she like all the others would die. Mother did not fight in her heart. She said, "It's no affair; if I die, I will go sit in the village of God." Hunger, our most cruel master, held us all helplessly inside his strong closed fist. Without food, what could we do? Could we build better shelters or make warmer clothing? When this time of trouble had passed, who among us would remain alive?

Then as God fed Elijah who had been driven by his enemies into the wilderness, so God saw our suffering and heard our cries. He sent ravens to help us. He brought us food from heaven.

One day when the sun was high, a new word spread among the people like fire driven of the wind: "They have come with food! They ask us to bring cups and bowls. They have a big truck. It is full of things to eat."

I did not go to get something to eat; I was hungry, but others needed food more than I. But I was curious to know if the rumors were true. I wondered who would do us such a good thing without wanting to ensnare us into something evil. Ndaya and her three children walked past with their bowls. I joined them. When we reached the truck, we read on its sides words in the white man's tongue: "Congo

182

Protestant Relief Agency." A white man was standing in the back of the truck on a hill of sacks filled with corn flour. Ndaya looked at him and started with surprise.

"That is the man who delivered us from our Lubumbashi troubles!" she said. "That is Lutongo!"

Fires were started. Corn flour was cooked in two great iron barrels. The hungrier made two long lines and they were fed. Each was given a bowl of hot mush and a cup of milk. They passed by, one by one, until the sun was low. They must have numbered a whole thousand. While Lutongo and his helpers prepared to leave, I went to introduce myself. I wanted to learn more about the work he was doing.

"I am David Mulumba," I said. "I am a mission pastor from Makala."

Lutongo smiled, grabbed my hand, looked at me eye to eye and said, "God has answered my prayers. We need you. We feed bodies of people, but we have no one to help us feed their souls. We want you to go with us."

"But how can I leave here when our people are suffering like this?"

"You see people suffering only in this one village," he replied. "You are helping them. This is good. But don't you want to help your tribesmen in many villages? Don't their souls need to be fed too? You can't finish your debt if you sit only in one place. Go tie up a bundle of things and come along with us."

"Do you feed people like this every day?" I asked.

"I am on the road feeding people every day," he replied. "We are putting feeding places in thirty villages, many of them larger than this one."

"But where does enough food come from to feed so many people?"

"Christians in other lands have heard of your suffering.

They want to help you. They are sending trainloads of food."

My ears were hearing these words, but my heart was slow to believe them. "And if I go with you, when will I come home again?"

"When we find a place here to keep food, we will leave sacks of it here with helpers; they will feed people every day. The truck will come with more food about every week. Whenever it comes, you can come with it and see your loved ones. Hurry, get your things. It is late."

I knew Ngalula could continue to help people if I left, and she could care for herself. But she could not do this and care for Mother as well.

"Is there medicine anywhere?" I asked.

"Yes, there is a large hospital at the town where we will be staying tonight. Why?"

"My mother is weak and ill; she cannot stay alone."

"Where is she? Let's go get her. We'll take her along."

Everything was happening so fast my mind was covered with fog. But everything sounded good. I led Lutongo along the path to our hut. He wanted me to walk faster. My heart was pounding.

I tried to explain everything rapidly to Ngalula. Here was an open door to heal countless souls. Here was a way to talk to more people than I had ever seen about Jesus Christ. Here was a way to help Mother. I told Ngalula to tie a bundle of my things and a bundle of Mother's things. She began obeying my words, though she had not yet understood them.

Lutongo and I entered the room where Mother lay on her mat. I began to pick her up.

"Can't she walk?" he asked.

"She hasn't been eating; she told us to keep our food for others."

184

Lutongo and I carried Mother to the truck. Ngalula followed behind with two bundles. I told friends good-bye along the way. We laid Mother on her mat in the back of the truck. A helper came and sat beside her to watch her. I climbed into the truck with Lutongo. He started the motor. He handed Ngalula a small box full of corn flour and the truck started forward with a great noise.

"Stay well," I shouted to her. "I'll return in a week."

We bounced along the road, the truck motor roaring. I was trying to clear up my mind to understand all that had happened this day. After a time Lutongo spoke.

"Do you know the trouble your country is in? The hoe has stopped its work of feeding; it is only doing its work of burying. Three hundred thousand of your tribemates are suffering from hunger. Two hundred are dying every day. One third of all your children will die in the six months which are ahead, unless they get food. We fed sixty-four hundred people today; we were at four different places. Every day, all our time is taken up by trying to keep people's bodies alive. Now you will feed their souls. You will preach the Word of God to them and pray with them. Those who die of hunger need not die in their sins anymore; they will hear about Jesus."

Thus he talked from time to time while we journeyed. The sun was setting; darkness would soon be coming. Suddenly Lutongo's helper was knocking on the window behind us and pointing to Mother. Lutongo stopped the truck.

"What's the trouble?" he asked.

"It's the sick woman," he replied. "She has died."

I stared at Lutongo; he stared down the road ahead of us. I began seeing fog. I bowed my head to weep in silence. After a few moments I felt Lutongo's hand on my knee.

"Pastor, she doesn't have hunger anymore. Her suffering is finished. She is happy and well in the village of God."

I knew this was true. I had been living close with death these many days. It no longer surprised me like a stranger. I felt inside that a part of myself had gone with Mother. But it was better now. Her suffering had ended and my own burden was lighter.

"What shall we do?" I asked.

"At the city where we are going, there are more dead than they can bury," Lutongo said. "All is sadness there. Let us find a tree along the road. Let us give her a quiet place to rest here away from the sadness of others. Then you will remember where the place is. You will remember it as the place where your mother entered her happiness."

There was a palm tree standing near the road ahead of us. We went to it and dug a hole beneath it. We folded Mother's blanket over her and lowered her on her mat into the grave. We closed the grave and sang one verse of the song, "When they blow the trumpet of God, I will be there." Lutongo prayed. We entered the truck. I looked back to see the grave again, but could not. It was hidden in the darkness. We continued on our journey.

The darkness that closed in on me that night did not break when the sun came up next morning. It closed in upon me for months. It folded itself around me tightly like the blanket in which we had enclosed Mother. It would not let me go. It sometimes enclosed me so tightly I felt weakness and could hardly breathe. It was the darkness of always moving among the dead and dying. It was the darkness of always giving my strength of life that others might live. It was the darkness of terrible war to defeat our enemy, Hunger, before he destroyed us as a tribe among tribes on earth.

At the town where we stayed that night there were thirty

186

thousand of our scattered people, sitting with their things. The hospital where I had hoped to get medicine for Mother was made sufficient for four hundred people. Inside it and lying outside it on the ground were two thousand sick people.

We went to a town on the southern frontier of our tribal area to give food to the suffering people; we had heard of tribal war there. We found that the town had been looted and burned. Strong buildings were empty shells, blackened with smoke, and poorer buildings were piles of useless rubble. About seventy people had been killed. Their bodies were scattered like broken carcasses of animals in the streets, waiting for someone to bury them. Hundreds of people were sitting beside pieces of wall or on the ground, as if dreaming, staring at nothing, their babies crying. Others of them lay in the hot sun, ill. The air carried the smell of death and of rotting flesh. Flies tormented everyone.

Other thousands of hungry tribemates had gathered at a nearby railroad town. Two railroad cars of corn and manioc flour had arrived. On that afternoon, one thousand people stood in line waiting for food when war broke out nearby. The hungry people fled to hide. Workmen who were helping us unload the food quit their work to join in the fighting or to help their families hide in the forest. After the war, a white-man doctor was brought in who had been shot three times in the legs and hand.

Many other things happened in those months of darkness, things you would not want to believe, things I want to forget. At last food sent to us by people of compassion in many countries began to reach us. Because of these gifts the darkness began to break and the grip of our slavemaster, Hunger, began to weaken.

From America came thousands of bags of rice and boxes

of dried milk and cans of cooking oil. Christians in Switzerland sent money which bought 20,000 blankets. Churches in Germany sent 970 tents as shelters for sick people. Belgium sent 2,000 crates of potatoes. Denmark sent a plane loaded with milk. Then came rice, beans, medicines, tons of Bibles and Scripture booklets.

At the city which was the storing place of all the things sent to help us, I watched with eyes which saw but refused to believe. Every day for part of a month ten great airplanes landed, emptied out forty-five tons of things, and left. They were like great white ravens sent by God, bringing us food to keep us alive in the wilderness.

After six months of hard fighting, we broke the back of our master. Hunger was beginning to leave us. Lutongo took me home. The journey back to my village was very different from the journey away from it. Here and there along the road we saw villages of tents. These tents were the homes of people—sacred places to those who lived inside them. These tents protected them well, until they could build houses of their own. Flowers, already blooming, had been planted outside some of the tents. Elsewhere, hillsides along the road were covered with groups of new huts. Their grass roofs made bunches of brown in the great blanket of green growing gardens which surrounded them. Yes, Hunger was truly leaving us. People were beginning to live like people again.

We passed one place where children were once dying and we had left tons of food. There was a new church built there now. It was full of people. Those who could not find room under the roof were standing outside. As we passed by we heard them singing:

> Draw us near to you, Jesus Child of God;
> Draw us near to You by the power of your blood.

188

I choked so tightly I could not swallow. All these things surpassed me to bear and my eyes filled with tears. I looked at Lutongo. He was looking hard ahead, but his eyes were the same. I knew my people would not forget. There were still the graves—everywhere. But our people did not sit looking at graves. There was too much happiness to look at graves. People had shelter again, Hunger was retreating, they had strength of body again. So they praised God.

The language of men had no words to describe how I felt. Angels of mercy had been sent to save us—angels with black skin, with white skin—angels in nations far away. God had angels everywhere. Working with them, He had brought us out of darkness. He had brought us back to days of happiness which we had feared we would never see again.

* * *

Like a snake without arms can climb a tree, so dead men, by struggling, can rise again.

17

It does not take a long time to change things when everybody works hard. A lizard, even though it loses its tail, soon is healed and continues on its journey. So we worked with one heart. The different kinds of work we did began to build our country again.

Soon traders came with trucks loaded full of merchandise. If we did not have money we would barter with them, using products from our fields. Thus a trader would sell us his things and leave with a truckload of manioc, corn, peanuts and beans. He would sell these things to people living in big cities, and then bring back another truckload of merchandise.

But traders could not bring enough things for everybody. Thus people took their field produce to public markets and exchanged it for things they wanted. Some of our people began to earn their livelihood by bringing things from faraway places and selling them at the markets. Thus the markets grew.

As the markets grew, people began to feel better. We would walk between the long rows of merchandise placed neatly on the ground—many kinds of bright-colored cloth, soap, salt, sugar, canned meats, dried fish, bicycle parts, perfume, drinks in bottles, livestock. We would tell ourselves, "Yes, the days of suffering are truly behind us. Those affairs are finished. We are progressing now."

Thus people struggled harder so that poverty would never catch them again. They made bigger fields to harvest more produce. They bought not only things their bodies needed, but they also bought things their hearts desired. Anyone still walking around asking for things was put to shame. "Everybody else has all they need," our people would tell him. "Why are you a beggar?"

Ngalula and I discarded our ragged clothing and bought new. From our box of nice things brought from Makala we took out tablecloths, sheets, bed and pillow covers and began using them. We replaced what we used with new things just as nice. Some of the nicest things in the box we did not disturb. I repaired my old bicycle and began using it again. Then I sold it and bought a new one. I bought goats and chickens. I even saved enough money to buy a small radio.

People began again the custom of coming to worship meetings. This also helped them forget their days of hardship. In our town of Kamuanga, men worked with one heart and built a large grass-roofed worship house. On Sundays there was not room for everyone. In the meeting, people would stand and declare that God had been good for He had delivered them from all of their troubles. Some would speak with tears of joy flowing down. Others confessed plainly that they had stumbled and asked to be forgiven and accepted again. Then someone would start a song and everyone would praise God, singing loudly. With joy they gave of their wealth, wanting to build a larger worship house of stone with a metal roof.

There was another sign that our part of the country was in the path of progress. We began receiving mail again. Shortly after I had arrived in our fatherland, I wrote my brother Mutombo. Now, these many months later, I received his reply. He was still doing the work of Jesus at the town of Lusama. There were not many of our tribe in high positions in that town, so when independence came, the local people did not drive away outsiders. Mutombo and Mbuyi now had a large family of nine children. They were well.

Mutombo had also received a letter from our uncles, Tshibuabua and Kabambi. They had not been driven away from their city of Kinshasa. They asked him if he knew what had happened to me. They wanted to write me about finishing the debt of Ngalula's bride-price.

"Look at these affairs," our people said. "Troubles have remained behind us. The very sick have died; the less sick have recovered. We have plenty of food. We buy whatever we want. We are receiving letters from distant places. We are praising God in a worship house again. Now we are on the right path. If we continue in this path, we will earn for ourselves happiness greater than what we knew before dipanda. Let's keep moving, tribemates. Let's never turn back."

People can fix up things at home, but they have no authority over things far away. One day news reached us which again caused us fear about what was ahead.

Every evening some of my neighbors would come to my house to hear the radio. This evening news came that Badibanga, one of our tribe who worked in the national government at Kinshasa, had been arrested. Badibanga was the eldest son of a famous chief of our tribe. He had been a champion fighting for independence from the beginning; because of this, he had been given a position of honor in the national government. His followers, mostly the young men of our tribe, supported him with hearts on fire. They said that because of his talents, someday he should be the leader of many. Now he was in prison, accused of wanting to stir up his people to rebel against the government.

"Did you hear that?" asked one who was listening.

"Dipanda is a hard affair," said another. "It has ruined

everything. Do we people here in the villages have any trouble getting along? No. It is the big people who know many books and pass over our heads in airplanes who can't get along together. A little firewood on top can burn up the whole pile, and so one chief on top can bring suffering to all those under him."

"Dipanda is not a bad thing," I said. "Don't you feel good that we are free? We are a nation among all nations of the world. We are men as tall as all men. No longer can someone come tomorrow and take from you your wife, or your child, or your things, while you watch as a dumb sheep. But trouble has caught us because those who ruled over us did not teach us how to rule ourselves. We don't know which of our leaders to follow, because none of them was taught how to lead. Dipanda is not bad. But the way we received it was bad."

"What you have said is true," said another man. "But the affairs of dipanda have brought danger to us all. This Badibanga is playing with the witch's palm wine tree. If he tries to climb it, he'll fall and break his neck."

Then a village elder spoke a fable.

"A she-leopard and a she-lion both had baby-stomachs. One day the leopard asked the lion, 'Where are you going to bear your young?' The lion said, 'Under the great tshimayi tree in the jungle. Where will you bear yours?' 'In the cave in the ravine,' the leopard answered. Each of them bore four cubs.

"One day the lion said to the leopard, 'Let's go take our offering to the chief's feast.' The leopard agreed. While they were walking together in the path the lion said, 'Why don't you go your own way and I'll go mine; we'll meet up ahead.' The leopard agreed.

"They left each other. Then the lion went to the cave in the ravine and placed the four leopard cubs in her offering sack.

193

The leopard went to the great tshimayi tree and placed the four lion cubs in her offering sack. They arrived at the chief's feast.

" 'Start the offering fire for us to dump in our offerings,' they told the chief. He ordered his servants to start the fire. Then the lion and the leopard dumped each other's children into the fire. When they saw it, they both left the feast weeping. Thus, if Badibanga does not come to agree with the national government, in the end they will be destroying each other's children for nothing."

We went to bed with troubled hearts. The days ahead could bring us peace, wealth in things and happiness that we had never known, or they could bring us civil war that would destroy all we had gained and us also. What would happen to us in the days ahead depended upon one thing— what happened to Badibanga. We prayed fervently that he and our national Bula Matadi would arrange their differences.

Things happened rapidly; we moved into a path which frightened us. Two nights later Kinshasa radio told us that Badibanga had escaped; he was being hunted. The next night we were listening to the radio station at Kalenga, the largest city in our tribal area. We heard the voice of Badibanga.

"My tribemates, you know well that I have worked hard for our freedom," he said. "Because of our hard work, we broke the white man's yoke of servitude from off our necks; we became free. We set up a government to rule ourselves.

"I was happy to be the one you chose to sit in our national government," he continued, "but that government no longer allows us even a tiny place. It no longer listens to my words. It counts us as a despicable tribe. It makes decisions about ruling us without asking me a question. Thus our voice to arrange our own affairs has disappeared. Again the yoke is being put onto our necks. Again we are being asked to submit as dumb animals.

"My fellow tribesmen, would you want me to live in a faraway city being a slave to others while telling you we were free? No. I fought for our freedom once, and we had hold of it. Now when they want to take it away from us, I will fight for it again. I want you to fight with me. We are one of the greatest tribes in the nation. The land of our forefathers is a rich land. We are many. We are strong. We have the heart to work hard. We can build our own country. We can drive off any who attack us. Death in such a struggle is not bad. If it must be thus, our blood will break the yoke with which others want to enslave us. Arise, my brothers! Let's go forward! Let's struggle until we stand free again!"

Badibanga spoke many other like words. He asked all young men who were willing to fight for our freedom to come see him.

Our older men said, "It is one thing to lift a foot; it is another thing to climb a ladder. Badibanga should not boast about eating until he has food inside his mouth."

But our young men answered the call of Badibanga. In the weeks which followed, most of them went to live in the forest. There they organized training camps where they learned how to fight. They returned to the village only for short visits or for food.

Then soldiers of the national government came. A group of them came to sit in each of our villages. Words were heard that outsiders were secretly bringing weapons to Badibanga's warriors. Soldiers began inspecting inside motor-cars and trucks which passed in the road, for hidden weapons. They told us to sit quietly in peace. They had been sent to finish the rebellion and to capture Badibanga.

When an elephant with tusks stands in the footpath, everybody welcomes him. We sat quietly.

But we knew that Badibanga and his helpers did not want peace. The earth began to tremble with uncertainty. People feared to go to their fields. They feared going to the stream for water. They stayed near their homes. They waited for the beginning of trouble.

Late one night some neighbors were sitting with me at my radio. One of our youth appeared, carrying a large basket of manioc.

"Before returning to the forest, I wanted to pass by here and see if there is any news," he said.

"There is no important news," replied one of my friends. "What news do you have? How are things going in the forest?"

"Things are going well," he said. "We have begun to do our work. Soldiers are trying to find us in the forest. This evening, on my way to the village for food, I saw five soldiers standing by a fire talking and drinking coffee. I prepared my gun for firing and sneaked quietly close to them. I aimed carefully and shot. Four of them fell. I hit the fifth on the side of his neck with my jungle knife. He was an officer. I cut his head off and took off his stockings; here are his stockings right here."

He pulled up his trousers legs and showed us heavy woolen stockings worn by soldiers.

Was this story true? There were the stockings. It must be true. When word of this killing reached the soldiers, it would mean one thing—war. Where would it start? Would it start tonight in the darkness? If it started, where would it stop? There were no answers to these questions. But anyone can tell when a storm wind begins blowing. It flattens the bushes and makes palm trees look like women whose hair

196

has been turned inside out. I went into the house, my mind whirling.

"Ngalula. Get up. There's going to be trouble."

I told her what we had just heard and seen outside.

"What shall we do?" she asked.

I thought hard to myself. I did not know.

"Perhaps we should take what food we can carry and go hide in the forest for a time," she said.

"But that is where the young men are hiding; that is where we know there will be fighting," I said.

"But what if there is an attack here in town tonight?" she asked. "People don't know who they are killing in the darkness."

I did not want to leave. "Here we have our livestock," I said. "Here we have stored sufficient food in the kitchen hut. We have our clothing, our beds, our sewing machine, our bicycle, our radio. We must try to keep our things. If we lose them, poverty and hunger will catch us all over again."

What direction would trouble come from? What path should we choose to follow? Any path could give us death or life. In hunting for the path of life, we were blind. After making a choice, we could not change it. We had to choose now. I prayed. I listened in my heart for what I hoped was an answer. I made the choice.

"Get the two large cardboard cases from under the bed," I said. "I'll get the large metal trunk from the kitchen hut. We'll pack what we can inside them. We will bury them here in the house. Then you will take some food and clothing and go to the forest. You will hide at the tall nsanga tree just beyond the corner of our field—the one near the stream. I will stay; I will try to guard our things and keep the livestock together. When a few days pass, if you have not heard the sounds of war, you may return. If trouble here becomes too great, I will join you in the forest. Doing it thus, we will see each other again soon."

We worked rapidly. We filled the cases and trunk. In them we placed the nicest things we had still saved from our days before independence—Ngalula's nicest wax dress and two skirts which remained, my preaching suit and the coat of my black suit and our bed clothing. Then we packed the sewing machine and a porcelain cooking dish among other clothing we had bought in the past few months. We dug a deep hole in the corner of our sitting room floor and buried the boxes. Ngalula took an extra dress, a knife, matches, a cooking dish, a blanket and a small basket of food. We said good-bye. She went out into the darkness.

War broke out in our town in the early morning of the second day. As the sun rose, fighting along the road was hard. It was coming closer. Every kind of gun was used: cannons boomed, mortars threw bombs which exploded, rifles cracked, machine guns stuttered, bullets and small pieces of iron flew through the air like hail. As I watched, I saw that one could not hide in a house in our town this day and remain alive. Was I craving our things too much? The elders say, The thing you love most will kill you. Even a snail, when it dies, can't take its house with it. I would leave the things. Though it would be very dangerous to go outside the house now in the light of day, I would have to try and escape.

I wrapped a knife, a shirt, my Bible and my radio into a blanket. I kneeled on the floor of our house and prayed. A bullet hit the wall of our house, then another.

"Lord Jesus," I prayed. "I have never caused a drop of anybody's blood to fall onto the ground. Now it appears that I may be killed uselessly. If you see in the midst of this trouble that I am innocent, then deliver me."

I took off my shoes so that I could run better. Carrying

them and my blanket bundle, I slipped out of the door. I stooped low, and sprang into the open, running. I ran for our field in the forest. As I passed our garbage pit, sharp pain stabbed into my left foot. I kept running, limping. I felt the warmth of blood flowing from a wound. I did not stop running until the hill separated me from town. Then I thanked God I still had life; I stood erect to breathe; I looked at my foot. Blood was flowing freely from a deep cut about two inches long.

I limped to the edge of the forest where no one could see me. I sat down to care for my foot. The cut was spilling much blood. I opened my blanket and took out the shirt. I tore a strip of cloth off the bottom of it and bound my foot tightly. Life would be better here in the forest, away from home, I told myself. Days of trouble pass exceedingly slow when one is alone. With Ngalula, the burden of trouble would be lighter.

After resting a bit, I followed along the footpath through the jungle. As I approached our field clearing I looked, hoping to see Ngalula near the field we had worked in together so many times. I crossed the field and I entered the forest and reached the tall nsanga tree. Ngalula was not there.

I circled the tree three or four times, hoping I was wrong. I saw no sign of her. I called her, fearing my voice would be heard by those who might do us harm. There was no answer. I went to the stream; perhaps she had gone there to bathe. She was not there. I returned to the tree again. I found a place beside a large root where the leaves had been pressed by the weight of her body.

There was no sign of struggling. Perhaps she had not been harmed. Perhaps something had made her go elsewhere. The pain of sadness in my heart was so great I felt no pain in my foot. I would wait. We had agreed to meet here. She would return.

But she did not return that day. Nor the next. Nor the next. Each day my foot became more swollen and painful. Every evening I bathed it in the stream; I wrapped it with a fresh strip torn from my shirt. Each day I became hungrier. Ngalula had the food we had planned to eat. Each day I heard the booming sounds of war from the direction of our town.

One morning while praying, I felt I must go elsewhere. There was a town some miles further. There had been no sounds of war from that direction. Perhaps Ngalula had fled there. Tribemates there would have food. If war had not yet reached there, perhaps they could care for us.

I cut down a strong straight stick with an open crotch on one end. I cut it the length of my armpit to the ground and wrapped the crotch with a large piece of my torn shirt. With this stick, I was able to walk, while resting my cut foot. I did not walk far that day. I ate berries I found along the way but their sweetness only tormented my stomach.

Late the next day I arrived at the village where I found the house of a friend. My body was very weak, but my foot felt better. My friend helped me sit in a chair and gave me water.

"Have you seen Ngalula?"

"Many women from your town have come here from the forest. I did not watch them closely. Perhaps Ngalula was among them."

"Where are they?"

"They have gone with many of our people into hiding. They have gone to a place where no trouble can reach them."

"All of our fatherland is in trouble, neighbor. What place is there that will not be troubled?"

"They have gone across the Lomayi River," he said. "They have followed its banks northward to the caves."

"What have you heard about the fighting?"

"It is spreading. For this reason we are fleeing. If you would have waited until tomorrow, you would have found here a town of empty houses."

That night I bathed my foot in salt water and bound it. I ate sufficiently. I helped my tribemate prepare his things to leave. I slept. I awoke early, hearing the boom of big guns far away. Many of the villagers were leaving on bicycle or on foot, carrying their possessions on their heads or on their backs. Because of my injured foot, my friend helped me find a place in a small motor bus. It was made to haul nine persons. With me, we numbered fifteen.

The driver drove rapidly, to separate us from the trouble coming behind us. We prayed the bus would not break down under this great load. We reached the Lomayi River only to find that someone had removed the boards from the bridge. Just the iron framework remained. Our hearts began to split with fear. Is this the way we all would die, here, openly, on the bank of a river?

The driver got out and called across the river. He called for a long time, while we prayed. He pleaded for someone to come save us. Finally someone came from behind a bush.

"Do you have any warriors?" he called to us.

"No!" cried our driver.

"Do you have any guns?"

"No!"

"Do you swear you are telling the truth?"

"I swear before God. I only beg you to save us."

Three other men came from behind a bush, carrying boards. They placed them on the iron framework. We crossed, thanking them. As we left, the men were carrying the boards back to their hiding place.

* * *

The cave was exceedingly dark. No one knew how large it was. No one knew all who were hiding in it. It swallowed as many people as came into it. Only when the entering place was opened to let in more people could I see outlines of those sitting close to me. Then bats, troubled by moving people, flew angrily about our heads.

When the entryway was closed and people sat quietly again waiting, sight was gone. We were enclosed by a living blackness that entered into our bones. One lived by hearing, hearing the loud never ending drip-drip of water from the ceiling; hearing babies, whimpering, then sucking happily from mothers' breasts; and by feeling, feeling the flit of wings of a diving bat; feeling the cold of wetness that seeped into our bodies; chasing away sleep and making our bones as sticks that would not bend. The few simple things that I had with me brought my only comfort—my radio, my blanket, my Bible and my leaning stick.

* * *

The troubles of each day, one following after the other, explain to us why we cried at birth.

18

For two whole months we stayed near the cave. I tried to show others a face of joy. I tried to lighten their burdens. From my Bible I read to them words of comfort. I reminded them that all these troubles had not destroyed God. He was still alive and with us. He was still able to hear when we cried to Him about our troubles.

They did not know that my helping them made my own burden lighter, for as I read them words from the Bible I too gained comfort. While my face was of joy, my heart was heavy with sadness. Inside myself, I was suffering.

Hunger bothered me like it did everyone else. More than this, my foot which could not be walked upon, which never stopped hurting me, weakened my heart. But there was something far worse than these sufferings. For these months of days—days which had the length of years—only part of me was alive. There had been no sign of my beloved Ngalula.

Thus when my radio told us from day to day that peace was being restored, my heart became more anxious. I wanted to go home. Ngalula might have come out of the forest by now. She might be waiting for me. If not, perhaps my bicycle would still be in the kitchen hut. It would help me travel until my foot was fully healed. With it I would go to all the villages around us searching for her. Somewhere, in one of them, someone would have word of Ngalula.

One day some of our men happened onto a trader with a truck who lived nearby. He agreed to take as many as he could in one trip back to our home villages. I was among the first to want to go. Returning, we passed through many villages which had been destroyed in the war. Many of these things I had seen before. I need not relate them to you. I was looking with my eyes, but not with my heart. In my heart, I had already arrived home.

As we reached the top of the last hill so we could see our home village, we of Kamuanga were stricken with exceeding grief. There was no village. There were no homes. There was only a space of bare ground following alongside where three roads met—a space which people once called, "the village of Kamuanga."

When we drew closer, we saw the piles of broken pieces of dirt which had once been our homes. From these piles, sticks which had been in the walls jutted upward. They were charred black and burned to ugly points. At some places weeds had grown high enough to almost hide the piles of rubble and one saw only the black sticks above them. At other places people had cleared away the rubble of their homes. They were pulling up the burnt sticks which could still be used and were driving them, along with newly cut sticks, into the ground. They were starting to build walls for their houses again.

The truck left all of us off at the intersection of roads. I started toward the end of the village where we lived. I put my blanket bundle under my arm and began running. Though my foot hurt, I ran this way and that, hunting a path between the high weeds and piles of rubble. The closer I got, the harder my feet pounded the ground in running. Suddenly I came into an open space where I could see well. I looked. There it was. My house was a pile of broken dirt and burnt sticks like all the others. I looked for Ngalula. She was not there. The kitchen hut had been only partly destroyed; its roof was tilted, one side of it resting on the ground where a wall had been. Ngalula would be in it; she would be sitting in its shade.

"Ngalula!" I cried wildly.

There was no answer.

She must be sleeping; she would be tired.

"Ngalula!" I called more loudly.

There was no answer.

I reached the hut, stooped and entered. It was filled with pieces of the broken wall. The food was gone. My bicycle was gone. Ngalula was not there.

I went outside and called again and again, each time louder than before. As I called her, I walked around and around what had been our home. There was no answer. This could not be true. Was I in a dream? I went into the shade of the kitchen hut and sat down on the ground. I wanted to rest and to think.

What should I do? I could hunt Ngalula, but I had no bicycle. I could hunt for food, but I was not hungry. I could begin clearing rubble to build a home again, but after I built it, would anyone be with me to live in it? Where was Ngalula? Was she dead or alive? If she were dead, would I want to live here in a new home alone? Was her body one of the many which had been thrown into holes in the ground? If so, someone would know about it. Among those present when such things happened, someone always escaped. Someone had a word to tell me about Ngalula. I would not have strength to build again until I knew what had happened to her.

For the hours that remained of that day, I talked to everyone I could find, asking the same question, "Have you seen Ngalula?" They all answered with the same one word, "No." When the sun set, one of them asked me to stay for supper; I ate little. In the darkness I found my way to our kitchen hut. Inside it, I cleared enough space on the floor to lie on. I rolled myself into my blanket on the ground and slept.

I was awakened by the sound of mourning. Someone nearby was crying the wail of death. I arose and looked out the hut door. I saw in the darkness the figure of a woman standing beyond the rubble heap. She was too thin for Ngalula. Some strange woman wandering around hunting for her dead mate, I thought. Then the cry came again, long and plaintive, and I recognized it as the voice of my beloved. I bounded from the hut.

"Ngalula!"

She screamed.

She collapsed.

* * *

The sun arose and found us rejoicing in being together again. Ngalula's body was thin with hunger, her dress was soiled and worn, but her heart was strong. She had been driven away from the hiding place we had agreed upon when a wandering band of warriors threatened her. She had gone deep into the jungle to hide. Now she had returned. I looked at her as if she had come back from the dead. We were together again. The bad dream was ended. The part of me that had died now sprang to life. Now I was ready to build again.

"It's time for you to take off those mourning clothes," I told her. "Let's dig up those boxes and find you a new dress."

With our hands we eagerly pushed the pile of dirt to one side until we found the place we had buried the metal trunk and cases. We dug down to them with our jungle knives. We reached the cases first. With much effort, I lifted the first one out. With fingers trembling from excitement, I opened its lid. Our clothing was covered with dirt. I unfolded the top garment and found that termites, building their tunnels of dirt, had burrowed through it. I carefully broke it away from the garment beneath it and held it up in my hands. It fell to pieces under the weight of dirt embedded into it. One by one we carefully took out the garments. We found them the breeding nest of an army of termites. Our garments were ruined.

The second case was the same. All the nice things we had so carefully saved since the good days at Makala were destroyed. From the metal trunk we found a skirt, the larger part of a bed sheet, the sewing machine and the porcelain cooking dish which we could still use.

Sadly we looked at each other. But why say "It's bad, it's bad," when it is all you have? Our faces changed. We had each other! Our bodies were strong. There was no more precious gift than this. Who cared about things? Lives could not be replaced. Things could be. With hard work, all these things would come back again, and more.

"Ngalula, wait with putting on the new skirt," I said. "First, let's clean out the kitchen hut; it will be our home for now. Then let's prepare a feast tonight—a feast in front of our home—a feast of rejoicing that we are together again."

By the time night arrived, we had cleaned the rubble from the hut. I had found two pieces of log—these would be our chairs. Ngalula, in her new skirt, was squatted at the fire cooking. In front of our hut, between our pieces of log, she placed her basket, its flat bottom upward. This would serve as our table. From the fire she brought the porcelain cooking dish with our meal—what she had found in our garden—three sweet potatoes. On our table they gave off steam and an odor that pulled water into our mouths.

Before eating, we sang "Come let us praise and worship God, and thank Him for His goodness." Then I lifted my words to Him, praying. Thus we ate our reunion feast. We had been to many feasts before, feasts for little affairs of happiness, feasts for remembering big affairs. But since we were born, we had not yet eaten a feast of happiness like this one.

Our happiness remained into the days that followed. We worked hard. We began to build again. The sun, when it rose from morning to morning, strengthened our hearts. We felt it was talking to us. It was saying that darkness had remained behind us and it would cause things to grow which would close over the scars of war. We saw its coming each morning as its promise to work with us; it would help us find again the things we needed for life.

Why can't the sun catch the hearts of men and rule over them? Then they would be friendly, honest and good, as the sun is. But it is not thus. Men who are not ruled by Jesus Christ are ruled by sin. Such men scatter suspicion, lies, enmity. They do not bless the earth, as the sun. They curse it. And people suffer.

Thus sin led the hearts of men, and without people seeing it a black cloud of storm again began to form. The black cloud grew until it threatened to swallow the whole sky and erase the sun forever and drench our groaning land again with the blood of people.

❂　❂　❂

It is useless to try to run away from the rain.

19

The trouble began between Chief Josef Kasavubu, presi-
dent of our country, and the men chosen to help him make
laws by which to govern us. Kasavubu said some of these
men refused to work with him. He said the group had failed
to establish the kind of laws the country needed. Because
these men refused to work in harmony with him, he took
from them their authority and dismissed them.

Some of these men had their own ideas about how to rule
our country. When Kasavubu dismissed them, they decided
to rebel against his authority and kill his government. They
would lay hold on his power and rule us as their hearts
desired. To do this work, some of them went and sat in the
big city of a country next to us; there they could sit in
peace, without being troubled by Chief Kasavubu or his
soldiers; there they began to establish their government.
Others of them fled in secret to their home villages within
our country. There they began to draw village people into
the path of revolting against the chieftainship of Kasavubu.

After Kasavubu dismissed the makers of laws, one moon
passed, a second and a third. There was little news of the
affair. We wondered what those rebelling against his government were doing. We were listening with our ears in
every direction. Some bits of news we would hear on the
radio, other bits we would read in letters received from our
friends sitting in other parts of our country and other news
we received from people passing by in the path.

In the first moon of the new year, we heard alarming news on the radio. To the west of us, a leader of those rebelling began to set up his kingdom. The rebel army gained authority over village after village, rapidly, as wind drives a fire. This rebel chief gained authority over two large tribes before the government army could restrain him. These tribes filled one part of our country which in the white man's tongue is called a province. The rebel warriors held firmly to what they had won. They were as little birds which cannot be driven from the jungle. The rebel leader set up his chieftainship over these tribes. As the elders say, If you can point your finger at it, you can build a house upon it. Thus, beginning with a little area, the rebel leader began to build his kingdom.

Soon after he had established himself, we heard a new voice speaking on the radio. Day after day it spoke the same message in many different tongues so that all our people would hear and understand. This is what the voice would say:

"Men of Congo, who ruined dipanda for us? Why do we suffer thus? By this time we should have big schools, enough for all our children, teaching them everything. We should have justice in our courts so when trouble catches us innocently, the guilty may be judged and punished. We should have places where things are made—the wealth of foreigners already having built factories so that everyone has work and no one sits idle. Every person should be sitting quietly in peace, knowing what he earns today will not be destroyed by war tomorrow. But instead of all this, what do we have? Trouble, suffering, war without ending.

"Those over us who could lighten our suffering, have they done anything to help us? No. While we are tormented in poverty, these greedy politicians have stuffed their pockets full. These good things which should be helping us, they have clutched in their own hands and used for their own happiness. Their desire is to let us suffer thus forever.

"Tribesmen, it will not be thus any longer. The time of your suffering is about ended. A new era has arrived. We are coming to help you. Welcome us into your villages. We will give you the kind of government free people deserve. We will build on justice, on honor, on truth. Friends of wealth from a far country are waiting to help us. They too love liberty. Men of Congo, rise up and help us. Together we will break the yoke of Kasavubu and his friends off our necks. We will destroy to the ground everything of his corrupt rule. Then we will build again. Then we will inherit the good things of freedom. Together let us build a country of riches and happiness."

While some of these accusations were true, we knew that he who boasts perfection has faults clinging to him. But affairs walk, as feet, following one after the other, and soon these few footprints were beginning to ruin the water in the whole stream. Our country became more troubled.

While the first rebel chief ruled in his kingdom to the west of us, other rebel chiefs began their work elsewhere. They made friendship with countries west, north and east of us. They sat peaceably across our borders in these countries and there they trained men who would fight with them. Then beginning at our borders, they expanded their kingdom. Some tribes fought against them and suffered greatly; other tribes joined them and made them stronger.

One rebel leader and his army captured the big city on the edge of the great lake on our border to the east. In the fighting, a great Christian leader from a tribe akin to ours was killed. He had been our champion in government. Other rebel armies entering from across the borders north and east of us, caught village after village, coming southward.

211

Then word came that thirteen tribes sitting north and east of us, as one man, had joined arms with the rebel leader coming from the east. Henceforth they would all have one name—Amputu. Now the affair of the rebels was spreading like fire of the dry season, fire that passed up even rain from heaven to extinguish it.

When these many tribes joined together to help the rebels, our hearts began to tremble. The stronger tribe among them had done evil work long ago. This was the tribe which for many years had caught people of tribes nearby and sold them as slaves to the Arabs. This tribe still ate food of friendship with Arab peoples.

One day a person passing by in the path showed us a piece of paper. He said copies of this paper were being scattered as seed among all the Amputu peoples. Here are the words of this paper.

WHAT EVERY AMPUTU TRIBESMAN MUST KNOW BY HEART

1. Every Amputu tribesman must know that he passes up all other tribesmen of Congo in having wisdom, strength of body and authority. He must always make people of other tribes know this by shouting and threatening them; thus the Amputu tribe will gain authority over them and enslave them.

2. We have one great enemy—he is the white man. If he had not interfered, all of Congo would already be under our authority. Beginning with the time when the Arabs were helping us, our race would have spoiled countries near us; we would now be ruling over them.

3. Despise money. Make it do for you the work of corrupting and bribing.

4. Never show honor or respect to those who say they work for God.

5. Hunt every way to rebel against people; thus they will recognize your authority.

6. Never enter into an agreement with anyone of another tribe. Trust only a fellow Amputu.

7. Never betray an Amputu.

8. Send Amputu to all universities of the world, but above all, to countries which agree with us and our aims. There our people will win many favors and progress rapidly.

9. When Congo comes under our authority, we will place all our tribemates in power. We shall humiliate those of other tribes who have studied much in school and want to share our authority. Thus we shall dominate all of Congo. We will enslave all its tribesmen for all eternity. Amen.

This was the promise the Arab slave hunter had made long ago to tribes which helped him. Were these tribes still holding onto this promise? This paper showed that those of the Amputu tribe had never forgotten it. We noticed that the rebel chief of this gathering of tribes had given himself an Arab name. Now we saw that he and his tribesmen had given themselves to fulfilling the ancient promise.

We asked ourselves, "Where do these rebel soldiers get their power?" Those who escaped from them said rebel warriors did not have big guns. Many times they wore palm fiber loincloths like our forefathers had made or they wore leopard skins. They tied palm leaves or pieces of animal hide around their heads. They conquered villages carrying only spears, knives, palm fronds and walking sticks.

The rebels said they were strong because they had secret medicine. They called it "dawa." Once we heard a rebel leader sitting across the border outside our country speak on the radio. He said, "The people of Congo are for us. They are sick of a corrupt government which has robbed and abused them. Let the supporters of Kasavubu's chieftainship bring their bullets and bombs. We are ready for them. In war, my fingers change to iron. I can make two hundred men fall with one sweep of my hand. All our warriors have taken pills which protect them from bullets. One dawa pill, and bullets are not able to touch them. Bullets change into drops of water."

Only their witch doctors knew the secret of this medicine. To fulfill these secret rites, they cut into the skin of warriors and gave them fetishes to hang onto their bodies. They taught them words to speak to invoke magic protection of the spirits when they went into battle. Witch doctors went with the warriors into battle to maintain the sacredness of these rites so that their magical power would not be broken.

Warriors had no doubts about the power of these medicines. Believing these things, they were afraid of nothing. They believed that if they were killed in fighting, after three days they would arise again.

Day after day, the rebel armies conquered many new villages. People who refused to join them were executed, their villages were plundered, burned and left wasted as if by a forest fire. It appeared that nothing could stop these warriors of magic. People began believing that what rebel warriors said about having powerful medicine was true. People feared greatly. Their hearts became as water, too weak to resist. Thus the rebel soldiers advanced rapidly.

Kasavubu saw that things were bad. He called for the rebel leaders to meet with his government to talk things over. He offered to give them a voice in ruling if they would stop the war. We prayed this would end the fighting. Leaders talked but they could not agree. A dog, whipped by its master, will go its own way; when it catches a scent, it follows it, running. After it sees the animal with its eyes, its master may call, but it will not return.

Thus the rebel armies went forward again. Larger villages

fell into their hands. Then they took Kisanganyi, the city which passed up all other cities in the northeast in largeness. This place became headquarters of the chief of all rebel chiefs. From here they would rule their kingdom.

We heard bits of news that when the rebels took a town, they caught its important people. One by one they killed them without giving them trial. They killed them in bad ways which were strange even to our forefathers. These words weakened our hearts.

One day two government soldiers passed through our village. "We saw the rebels coming—hundreds of them," they said. "We shot and shot, but they kept on coming. As they came closer, we felt something burning in our chests. There was nothing to do but run from them." If soldiers with big guns could not stop them, how could we simple village people?

Perhaps these stories of what the rebels did to those they captured were made bigger when passed from person to person. Perhaps these soldiers had really deserted the government army and made up this story to justify themselves. Perhaps all these stories were false. Perhaps they were true. We did not know.

The radio spoke again. The great rebel chief was going on a journey. He was going to visit all the large cities of his kingdom. The people in these cities were planning a great welcome for him to thank him for helping break off the yoke of Kasavubu's play government. Other rebel chiefs had gone on journeys to North Africa to sit with leaders of countries there. These leaders were arranging ways of helping the rebels finish their work of conquering our country.

There was not much work left for them to do. The village of Lusama was taken. This meant that Mutombo and his family were in their hands. By this time, rebels had overrun villages in three-fourths of our country. Only the big city of

Malandi, a short journey west of us, remained between Lusama, to the north, and the province to the west where the first rebel chief still sat, ruling his kingdom.

If the rebels took Malandi, they would join hands with the rebels in the western kingdom and thus would cut the country into two pieces. Then who would restrain them from fulfilling their promise of bringing all the people of Congo to submit to them for all eternity? We who remained would be as crumbs which needed to be swept up. The rebel chiefs would be as men who had eaten well, who were now sitting back, resting, cleaning their teeth. Meanwhile we had no peace. We did not sleep well. The whole earth trembled.

Then suddenly, something happened which we were not able to understand. We heard news of a short battle north of Malandi. The rebels did not arrive at Malandi. Instead, they ran fleeing back north to Lusama. The government army began to move forward, like an elephant in the jungle, slowly breaking a path where it chooses, crushing trees beneath its feet. Little by little, people began lifting their eyes to see that truly, the storm was receding.

We began looking at each other in amazement. What surprising thing had, at one time on one day, turned this whole affair backwards? What was it that had passed up the rebels in strength, broken their power, and chased them, fleeing?

Among the many things I had heard on the radio in these days of trouble was news that my friend of long ago, Daniel Tshisanga, was ill. He was in the hospital. When I heard this news, I remembered the day when I was a class child, when Tshisanga came to the mission post. I remembered the words he taught us which caused me to open my heart to Jesus. Many things had passed since then. He was an old man now. In these many years I had not found time to go visit him. Now I wanted to go to Malandi to see him, while he was still alive. Perhaps seeing me would strengthen his heart. Then I would be able to ask the people of Malandi what had stopped the rebels, turned them around, and chased them away.

* * *

To draw the picture of a pretty house is easy; to build it is hard.

20

A trader picked me up in his truck and carried me to the middle of the city of Malandi. I got out of the truck and asked the way to the house of Daniel Tshisanga. As I came closer to it, I noticed the yard was full of people. I went near to a man standing where the path entered the yard.

"Is this the home of Daniel Tshisanga?" I asked.

"Yes."

"Is he still in the hospital?"

"No."

"Where is he? I'm his friend of long ago. I've come to see him."

The man looked at me without saying a word. Then he looked at the ground. "He's dead."

"Dead? When did he die?"

Still looking at the ground he said, "He died the night before yesterday. We buried him yesterday."

I had arrived too late. I found a chair among the many people who had come to mourn. I sat for a while. I prayed, arranging my thoughts. I had to go speak words of comfort to his widow. When I felt some strength return to my body, I rose and passed slowly among the many people. I entered the house. Mrs. Tshisanga sat on the floor, as is our custom at such times. Around her sat a circle of women who had come to comfort her. I told her who I was, shaking her hand in both of mine. My voice choked; we spoke to each other with our eyes.

She showed me to her son, Kabasele. He was a grown man. When he learned who I was, he drew me to himself, sorrow trying to overcome him.

"Your father was a champion," I said. "He would want us to be brave."

"His heroism for Jesus leaves us all feel guilty," he replied. "It strengthened everybody who knew him. He showed this heroism to the end of his days upon earth, even when the rebels were in the path to catch us."

"Tell me about this. I haven't heard."

"Truly, I forgot. You are a stranger in our city." After thinking a bit he said, "Could you return Tuesday? Let the weekend first pass. Let our guests return to their places. Then I will tell you."

I did not want to pass too many days away from home. My own heart was troubled about my brother Mutombo and his family. The national army had driven the rebels from the town of Lusama. I knew that now Mutombo would be sending me some word. But I did not want to return home without learning why the rebels failed to conquer Malandi. What part had Tshisanga had in this affair?

"I will return Tuesday," I said.

On the day of the Lord, I joined the great crowd of people worshiping in the big city church. There was no room for more people. We sat close together, as beans in a cup. In the meeting a man stood to speak. He had just escaped from the part of our country to the west of us, which had been in the hands of the rebels from the beginning of these troubles. He had lived under the authority of the rebels for almost a year.

When this man was in much trouble, he had made a vow to God. He promised God that if his life were spared and he could again meet and worship with his brothers and sisters in Christ, he would stand before them all and glorify God;

219

he would give God an offering of thanks. Now because God had delivered him, he was fulfilling his vow.

I wanted to talk with this man. It was my good foot of luck to learn what was inside this affair of revolution. When we finished worshiping, I hunted him until I found him. Other people were already talking with him; they wanted to learn more about the rebels too. He agreed to meet with us that afternoon. We were to meet him alone at the home of a Christian.

When we arrived that afternoon, we were taken to a circle of chairs in the sitting room. We seated ourselves and waited. The man began his story.

"I am a layman. For many years I have worked at the mission post of Mukendi. I remember the day two rebels first visited us. They shared with us their plans. We thought it was a good affair. You yourselves know that the troubles which have caught us since independence have weakened the hearts of all of us. Now these two men told us that the good things of independence had been denied us and were being squandered by selfish politicians who were over us. The conduct of these leaders had now shown everybody that they were traitors. The good things of true independence were still present. We would have to take them by force from the hands of those who held power over us. These things would come into our hands when the revolution succeeded.

"These revolutionaries told us that when they ruled, people would again fear laws and respect each other. There would be schools for all our children and work for every man. They promised to right all the wrongs which had troubled us. Their words showed us that they understood our problems. Most people believed their words to be true. We agreed to help them. We were as the hunter who welcomed the snake, not knowing he would be bitten by it.

"Thus leaders of the revolution began to live among us. Secretly, they called young men to be soldiers. There were thousands of youths among us who had not received places to study in school. They sat idly in the villages, with no way of improving themselves. Now almost all of them joined the army of revolution. Thus they had work in their hands. They had something to do. They joined together with one heart. They wanted to build a new country, a country in which they could progress. They were building it for themselves and for all of us.

"Our youths left their villages. They disappeared into the jungle. There, in gathering places hidden from the eyes of outsiders, they studied. They learned the laws of fighting this kind of war. They told no one of the things they were learning. They seldom returned to their villages. They came only to bring messages, to get food and to find other youths who would join them.

"Thus the youth army grew and prepared itself for war. In the white man's tongue such youth are called *jeunesse*.

"Meanwhile leaders of the revolution began planning the government which would rule when the revolution began. Our section of the country was divided into different parts. Each part was to be ruled by a man called a zone commander. These men were placed in their areas. They arranged themselves to make laws and rule over their zones. Only the big chief of the revolution, called the supreme commander, was over them. They sat quietly and waited for the time for them to begin their work.

"The leaders had told us that the revolution would succeed only if we guarded the affair among ourselves; foreigners among us must know nothing about it. We didn't want to keep things secret from the missionaries for they had always been one with us. But this affair did not concern the missionaries. It concerned our own country and its rulers. We believed it was for the good of our people. We followed the proverb of our fathers which says, Don't tell a stranger your secrets; another day they will show up in your home village and humiliate you. So we swore among ourselves to keep all these things secret.

"When the time was sufficient, the youth army or *jeunesse* began its work. Later we came to know what our youth had been studying in the jungle. They did most of their work at night. They burned bridges. They blocked roads by digging pits across them or felling large trees across them. They said this was important so that government soldiers could not come in and interfere with the work they were about to do.

"Then one night they began attacking and burning government meeting places that were not in large towns. They used their jungle knives and spears and killed men working for the government who lived there. We did not like to hear of these killings, but those leading the revolution said these things had to be done at the beginning. They said these men had grown fat on the money and gifts of our traitor government. While they, as antelopes, suffered with swollen udders, we, the bearers of children, always had empty breasts. To arrange these bad affairs, these men had to be done away with.

"Then the *jeunesse* made war with people living on mission stations. They burned school buildings and places of worship. They said men over them had ordered them to destroy everything. They said that after their foreign friends came to help them, when only a few months had passed, buildings nicer than these would rise again out of the earth.

"Because of these conditions, missionaries suffered. A few

222

were killed. When they suffered thus, they fled. We did not know they would be caused to suffer. We thought they would need to leave only for a short time until the revolution succeeded. But when they left, many people came looking for the things that were in the missionaries' houses. 'The missionary always kept these things for himself; the time has come when these things should make everybody happy,' people said. So they broke the doors and windows in the missionaries' houses and took all their things.

"In driving out the missionaries and taking their things, our people were as the villagers who saw a bird and thought it was ugly. But its song was pretty. After living with the bird for many days, they coveted its song. So they killed the bird to steal its song. The song died too, and they had nothing.

"Some of our church leaders began to have doubts about the revolution. Its prettiness disappeared when they saw it close up. If rebels were against the missionary, were they against the worship of God? Would the big chiefs of the revolution let those who worshiped Jesus follow their hearts and sit at peace? We saw that it would be well for us to inquire about these things. The church chose five of us. We went to see the supreme commander of the revolution. We were three pastors and two laymen. We walked to his headquarters, hidden in the jungle.

" 'Now that the white man is gone, we want to understand better about the revolution. Will it hinder us from worshiping God, as is our custom?' we asked him.

" 'Has anyone interfered with your worshiping?' he asked.

" 'No.'

" 'When the white man was with you those many years, did he not teach you how to do your work of God?'

" 'He did.'

" 'If he taught you well, now that he has left, why should

your work die? Go back to your places and do your work. If I have any other word for you sometime, I will inform you.'

"Later word reached us that when we had left, the supreme commander said, 'The heads of those men are too full of teachings of the white man. If too many people like that stay alive, our revolution will not progress well.'

"Little by little, people of the villages became enslaved by the warriors and the chiefs of the revolution. They were forced to feed the *jeunesse* warriors. They were forced to do every kind of shameful work for them. If anyone refused, he was beaten or he was caused to kneel on the ground in the hot sun and hold his hands in the air while hours passed. If a warrior wronged a village person, the villager went and told the zone commander. Leaders of the revolution had promised justice, but now, when the leaders of the revolution were in power over us the village person was always found to be guilty, and the warrior was left go without penalty. Thus villagers began to have serious doubts about the revolution. They remembered the proverb which says that pretty roof peaks can hide many faults.

"Village people also became troubled because they couldn't buy the things they needed. Chiefs of the revolution had promised us that they would soon have the larger towns in their hands. They had shown us the day of the moon when this town or that city was to be taken by our warriors. But rubber sap is easy to get; elephant tusks are hard. Government soldiers in the cities were many; their guns were big. *Jeunesse* warriors were unable to drive them out. Many of our youth died in the fighting. Thus because we were separated from the big towns, people could not buy kerosene for their lamps, or soap for bathing, or cloth to cover their bodies, or salt for their food. Because the roads had been ruined by big holes and felled trees, traders with trucks could not bring us these things.

"Thus people began feeling within themselves that leaders of the revolution were truly turning things upside down; but their work of turning things upside down did not increase our joy, it increased our suffering. We began to see that these men were rebels against the government, truly, but they were also rebels against us. We no longer saw that their work was helping us. When they, like vultures, showed their claws, they lost their reputation.

"One day chiefs of the rebels sent a message to leaders of our church. It was not wrong for us to gather together for worship, they said. But we should not pass too much time in church. We should finish worshiping more quickly; people needed to stay at their work longer these days, to help the revolution.

"When other days had passed, they sent another rule. It was not good to ring the church bell or to beat the calling drum to gather people for worship. All our people knew the times they were to gather for worship. Such useless noises troubled people who did not desire to come to church.

"Another affair which weakened people's hearts was their poverty. Rebel chiefs sent another rule. It was not good for a few people to have many things while many people had nothing. Those who had wealth would now divide it with those who needed things. As an example, each man could have only two pairs of trousers. He could wear one while he washed the other; he needed no more. He would give his other trousers to people who needed them. Rebel chiefs sent their workers to help people divide their wealth out to others.

"Our people did not like this law. Some of them accepted it, saying, 'Keep wearing the loincloth you have, my brother; the path to the store has become long.' Others rebelled against it, saying, 'We ate friendship with the rebels to increase our palm nuts. How is it that now they say our palm nuts are theirs?'

"Rebel leaders tried hard to wipe out such thoughts of rebellion. One morning a man who had spoken such words was found dead in his home; someone had shot him. Then from time to time, a person who had spoken such words would disappear during the night. Those near him were afraid to talk about what had happened to him. One rebel chief did not like a certain family. A person in this family had mistreated him long ago. Now, one by one, every person in that family was killed.

"Rebel chiefs accused our mission teachers of spreading bad words among the people and weakening their hearts. Thus rebel leaders forced schools to be closed. They accepted for no one to go near the class buildings. Children sat uselessly at their houses. People found reading books were caught, questioned and threatened. Rebel chiefs told our teachers to support the revolution or trouble would catch them. Other important people who had a strong word among the villagers and opposed the rebels disappeared, one by one.

"By this time, many of our youth and older children had been killed in the fighting. Rows of them, shoulder to shoulder, with bows, arrows and spears, went singing into the fighting. Guns killed them all. Behind them came others, trampling their dead tribemates under their feet. They too were killed. Thousands and thousands were killed in different places where there was fighting. Sometimes their bodies were thrown on top of each other, making a hill. Then gasoline was poured onto them and they were burned so that sickness would not begin to kill others. Even though all of these had died, rebel warriors had failed to chase government soldiers from the larger towns.

"On top of this, people whispered that government soldiers were standing like a fence, all around our part of the country. They were stronger than our youth who remained, thus the fence encircling us was becoming smaller and smaller.

"When rebel chiefs saw that so many people were dying, they sent out another law. All *jeunesse* warriors were to take village girls to be their wives. They were to make the girls have many babies, to replace the youth lost in the fighting.

"Parents complained that their children had been killed. They accused the rebel leaders of having killed them for nothing. Thus warriors raided new villages and kidnapped children. They brought these children to the complaining parents and said, 'You are crying about children; take these and sit quietly.'

"One day word came from the supreme commander. He wanted to see our church leaders. They obeyed, fearing as sheep answering the voice of a stranger. They arrived at the place where he was sitting. At that time a woman was making a complaint to him.

" 'It has always been the custom that when a big chief wants to establish his kingdom, he shows himself to the people everywhere so they praise him and render him homage. A chief people respect must be a chief of the people. But what kind of a kingdom are you trying to establish, hidden here in the jungle like this?'

"The big chief became drunk with anger. He finished it by pouring it onto people. He gave a word. His men shot and killed the woman. Our leaders watched and remembered that he who passes heavy sentence is the one who is guilty and that he who refuses to borrow wisdom will lead people astray.

"The supreme commander gave a new law to our pastors: 'Beginning now, you must preach affairs which strengthen

227

the revolution,' he said. 'Your Bible teaches much about revolution. Look at the people of Israel. Did they not oppose their wicked masters in Egypt? Did they not break off the yoke of slavery by violence and rebellion? Look at Jesus. Did He not give His life to destroy injustice? Did He not defend the poor and suffering people of His day? He was a great revolutionary. Beginning now, we will send our helpers to sit in on your worship services. They will help you teach the people things they need to know.'

"The pastors began their journey on foot back to the mission post. While returning, a group of rebel warriors caught them and beat them. When they arrived at the mission post and told what had happened, our people were very angry. Are dogs, who obey when they are called, beaten? Leaders of this revolution had treated our honored men worse than dogs. These revolutionaries are ruled by demons. They are insane. They don't respect the rights of others. They say that a person is the common property of all people; they ignore the truth that he belongs to the Creator. They despise the laws of God and of our forefathers. If their affairs progressed thus for three or four years, who among us would remain alive? Would anyone remember the laws of Mvidi Mukulu? Would this revolution not wipe out forever the kingdom of Jesus Christ?

"Now all of us in our hearts agreed that the revolution was bad. What had tasted good in the mouth was now sickening the stomach. But what could we do? It was too late to escape being mixed up in it. One with a lame leg could not accuse another with a crooked nose for our trouble. We were all guilty. We were trapped as ants inside a bottle. What paths could we follow in trying to deliver ourselves?

"We could continue helping the revolution. We could say with our mouths and do with our hands things our hearts

228

did not like. Thus perhaps our lives would be spared. But this would be like each one of us hoeing with two hoes.

"We could flee to the jungle and into the high prairie grass and hide, hoping the rebels would not find us. Then we would not have to do things which tormented the voice in our hearts. But there hunger and sickness would catch us.

"Or we could oppose the revolution. They would torment us, they might kill us, but then our mouths and hands would agree with our hearts as one. If we died, we would have no debating within ourselves or with God. This was the path we would try to follow.

"We arrived near the season of Christmas. We refused to act like people who had never heard about Jesus. We decided to rejoice on His birthday this year as we had done all other years. When the day arrived, we rang the bell loudly for a long time. Then we beat the calling drum hard. We wanted to tell everybody. On that big day we did all the things we had done every year for the many years before these troubles caught us. We passed the day in the house of God. Our pastors did not preach hatred and fighting. They preached that God loved everybody and He had sent His Son to earth to destroy the kingdom of sin. We sang loudly. We had all agreed among ourselves that if the rebels wanted to kill us, they should kill us in the house of God.

"The rebels did not bother us at this time. When they saw our stubbornness, they devised other means to humble us. Rebel leaders arranged a row of names of important persons who were hardening people's hearts against the revolution. These people were to be killed. There were sixteen names. The first person named was our chief. We, his people, number about five thousand. As the anvil stone of the blacksmith belongs to the whole village, so our chief belonged to all of us. We lived in villages surrounding the mission post.

"When our chief knew that they had marked him to be killed, he acted wisely. A rebel zone commander sent him a message. It asked the chief to come discuss some matters. This was their clever way of planning to kill him. Our chief did not go. He was as the rooster which has a hard heart because it had been sleeping in the house of those who wanted to eat it. Instead he sent the rebel commander his reply: 'Please come with your helpers and see me; then my tribal counselors and I will be happy to discuss whatever problems are troubling you.'

"Our chief sent his note in the hand of a young girl. This is our custom in such cases. The girl is impartial; she cannot be accused of being mixed up in either side of the dispute.

"When the rebels received the note, they became terribly angry. Their plans had been frustrated. They cut off the girl's head. They stuck it onto the end of a post and set up the post along the side of the road where our women, coming from the fields that evening, would see it.

"The man who hangs the one he has killed from the branch of a tree blackens the name of his whole village. This act was a terrible insult to our people. It tied them together as one man. They were enraged. Our men went to war. They attacked the place where this rebel leader sat. They burned his buildings to the ground. They chased the rebels.

"Some days passed. Then early one morning, when it was still dark, many rebels came to fight us. They encircled the mission post and the villages nearby. They set fire to the hospital and the school buildings and entered the church where they stacked the wooden seats in the center and set them on fire. They passed us up in numbers. We could not resist them. We all fled, to hide in the jungle.

"All of us did not escape. They caught a pastor, six other men and me. They tied our hands hard behind our backs and beat and kicked us. They took us to their zone commander for trial. We were accused of stirring up people to revolt against the revolution. Our trouble was great. At this time I vowed to God that if ever I would have the happiness of being free among His people again, I would stand before them and glorify His name, and I would give Him a big offering of thanks.

"The judges condemned five of the men to die. The pastor was accused of teaching bad things; he was to be punished. We were taken onto the prairie. There we stood, our hands tied, under the hot sun. The five men were made to dig holes in the ground. Then they were thrown into the holes, and while living, were buried. Another hole was made for pastor. He was buried in manure and garbage until only his head stuck out. He suffered this way until the sun went down. My friend and I were beaten. When darkness came, they pulled pastor out of his hole. Our hands were untied. That night I sneaked between two rebel guards. I fled deep into the jungle. I didn't rest until I crossed the river to where the rebels had not yet arrived. I fell to my knees and cried with tears falling to the ground as rain. I thanked God. He alone had delivered me."

His story was finished. Who had ever heard of slavery that caused people such suffering? My heart split when I came to understand that this was the slavery which had threatened to catch all of us.

❊ ❊ ❊

When you put your foot into a coil of rope, you can't complain when it has caught you.

21

On Tuesday I returned early to the house of Tshisanga.
The guests had gone. Kabasele and I were alone in the yard.
We sat on two chairs placed beneath low shade trees to one
side. Kabasele began his story.

"When news of the rebellion first arrived, people were not
troubled. They said, 'The sickness isn't mine, it's my clans-
man's; he's far away.' They had been wearied by the wars
which followed after dipanda. They did not want to think of
fighting again. They had homes. They had work—some in
offices, some in stores, some in their fields. The stores here in
the city were full of things to buy. The streets were full of
people with happiness. Missionaries and other white people
were living among us doing their different kinds of work.
Thus we saw that all was well.

"Then signs of trouble came closer. We heard about the
work the rebels were doing. Then we heard of the soldiers
fighting them. Bodies of soldiers killed in the fighting were
brought here to be buried. Their coffins were covered with
big flags. Trucks carried them down our streets. Following
them were trucks full of soldiers, watching silently. Along
the sides of the streets, people stood and watched and
thought.

"When rebels began causing missionaries to suffer, many
missionaries fled to our city for refuge. They told us plainly
what the rebels were doing. Three missionaries were cut in
pieces with jungle knives. A lady missionary was shot in the
neck by an arrow and died. A missionary airplane pilot was

shot and killed. Nearly all the missionaries escaped with their lives, because they were able to flee.

"But our village people suffered greatly. Their suffering surpassed their strength to bear it. They were many. They had no cars or airplanes and could not flee. So many of them sat in their villages, waiting, trusting the wisdom of their chiefs. Some chiefs did not want to help the rebels. So some of them were beaten until they died; some of them were buried in the earth, being with life; some of them were beheaded.

"When the city of Lusama fell, fear caught all of us. It is the last large town north of us. The rebels sent us a message by radio: 'On the third day we will arrive at Malandi,' they said. 'Arrange yourselves for our arrival.' They had the custom of doing this, to cause people ahead of them to fear. Nearly all times, they arrived on the day they had promised. We were as tiny orphaned chipmunks, trembling in our den, a he-lion standing at the entryway.

"The army began to arrange itself to guard the city. Everyone knew that if Malandi was taken by the rebels, it would be a hard affair to deliver our country from their hands. Soldiers put on their fighting clothes. They wrapped their bodies with belts of bullets. They tied stalks of grass to their iron hats so they could lie in the grass unseen. They fixed their hands to their guns.

"Other soldiers dug a line of big holes in the ground in front of the airplane terminal, facing north, the way from which the rebels would come. They dug holes in front of the radio station. They entered into these holes and sat, holding their guns. Some held small guns that stutter, spitting bullets. Others sat behind big guns mounted on legs of iron. Other soldiers unrolled circles of wire across roads by which the rebels would come—wire with barbs sharper than the thorns of jungle vines which tear flesh. A soldier sentinel with a gun that shoots far climbed up onto the roof of the airplane terminal and kept looking to the north, hunting with his eyes. Everyone knew the rebels were in the path, coming. The army had obeyed their message. It had arranged itself for their arrival.

"In our city there are about one hundred thousand people. Many among them had hearts to help the rebels. One day I heard a man say, 'The ones who always kill are not rebels coming from far away; they are the soldiers who live among us.' The army knew that many people among us had hearts to help the rebels. People began telling each other that there was only one way to save the city from being taken by the rebels. The army would have to kill all the rebels' helpers before the rebels arrived. Then those who remained would fight with the army and save the city.

"When this news spread among the people, everyone disappeared. Some hid inside their homes, keeping doors and windows closed, as if they had gone on a journey. Many others fled to hide in the jungle or in the high prairie grass. Our streets became empty of people. Storekeepers did not unlock their front doors; they stayed hidden inside. Army jeeps passed slowly through our streets. On the back of each car a soldier sat behind a big stuttering gun on iron legs, with a belt of bullets passing through its mouth. Our city became as dead and silent as a corpse.

"White people, being as visitors among us, did not want to be caught by the rebels. One day a big airplane came and took away all the Belgian white people who had been helping us. Another day a big plane came and took away the United Nations people who had been helping us. Then we feared the missionaries would leave too. We begged them to stay. If they left, perhaps everybody would be killing everybody without restraint, as had happened when they had left because of the troubles with dipanda.

234

"Many missionaries were in our city at this time. They gathered into a meeting to talk and pray. After fighting inside themselves, they agreed to stay with us. They said they would try to keep working for God, regardless of the kind of people ruling over us. Then together they stood and pledged themselves singing, 'Jesus, I Have Promised to Work for You Until the End.'

"Their promise strengthened our hearts. My father was in the hospital. His heart sickness was troubling him again. But another affair troubled him also. When a missionary came to visit him, he spoke to him of it.

" 'Doesn't God have power today like He had long ago?' Father asked him.

"The missionary paused and then replied, 'Why, yes, God has the same power today that He has always had.'

" 'If God has the power today that He had long ago, can't He chase away these rebels?'

"The missionary paused, thinking, and replied, 'Yes—if it is God's will, He is able to turn them back.'

" 'You missionaries ought to gather together to pray. You ought to pass a whole day in prayer. Let us see if God won't do something for us today like He did for the disciples of Jesus as we read in the book of Acts in the Bible.'

"The missionaries gathered themselves together. They gave themselves to prayer. Only two days remained for the rebels to arrive.

"On the morning of this same day, five big trucks filled with soldiers began the journey northward to hunt for the coming rebels. The night passed. In the afternoon of the following day, word reached us that an amazing thing had happened.

"The soldiers had passed the night lying in their tents at a place where two roads cross. When morning came two trucks filled with soldiers continued the journey. If the rebels were to arrive at Malandi tomorrow, as they had promised, they would have to be in the road coming today. The soldiers kept riding northward, watching. The road ahead of them turned and disappeared in the high grass.

"They followed the sharp curve and suddenly saw eight trucks filled with rebels, coming at them rapidly. There was no time to find a hiding place. There was no time to flee. There was no time to think, 'What shall we do?' Quickly as seeing it with their eyes, they raised their guns toward the rebels and shot and shot, throwing as many bullets as their guns could throw. They fought hard, not wavering. The rebels fell, bleeding. After a short time had passed, rebels in seven trucks had fallen, dead or wounded. Those remaining had no strength. Their hearts splitting with fear, they climbed into the truck which remained. In the truck, they fled northward, as ants trying to escape before an anteater.

"Thus our city was saved. It did not escape because of the strength of guns. It did not escape because of the strength of people. We saw it was saved because my father had strong faith, faith which told the missionaries, 'You meet together and pray; see if God won't do some surprising thing like He did in the olden days.'"

When I heard the story of Tshisanga's faith, my own faith was strengthened. But now my heart was trembling to return home. I wanted to eat the food of Ngalula. But more than that, I wondered about Mutombo, Mbuyi and their children. Had they passed through the revolution without being harmed? Perhaps by now some word had arrived.

A day passed until I found a trader's truck beginning a journey toward Kamuanga. I arrived home when the sun was lowering and people were returning from their fields. I got out of the truck and saw Ngalula pounding manioc flour at the mortar in our yard behind the house. I started for her when I saw another woman seated near the wall of my house, in the shadow of the roof which passed low over her head. Around her were children, sitting on the ground.

"Who are these guests?" I asked myself. I walked slowly, to see her better. She arose and began to walk slowly toward me. It was Mbuyi, the wife of my brother. Those were her children. She looked like an old woman; her body was wasted, her shoulders were stooped, her face was sad. As she came closer, her eyes spoke many deaths. She wanted to fall at my feet. I caught her and held her, helping her back to her chair. She sat heavily, as one who had no mouth to tell of her sorrow.

"Where is Mutombo?" I asked.

She paused, looking down at her folded hands.

"He has gone on ahead of us," she said.

"I don't understand."

"They killed him."

❋ ❋ ❋

Covet hip meat and you'll end up eating feet bones; eat fast and you'll burn your mouth.

22

I did not want to accept this news. I remembered how fighting had separated Ngalula and me for many days. We thought each other was dead. This happened to many people. But when war is finished, people return from where they are hiding and those who love each other come together again. I wanted to tell Mbuyi that it would be thus; after some days, Mutombo would come from his place of hiding. She and the children should stay with us. When the time was sufficient, he would find them here.

But I restrained myself from saying anything now. Mbuyi's burden was great. I did not want to say anything that would make it greater. So I sat quietly. Though our mouths spoke no words, our hearts comforted each other.

We sat thus while night came. Ngalula did her work in the kitchen hut preparing food. When she brought it, the children ate. I ate nothing. Mbuyi ate nothing. When the dishes were taken away, we sat again comforting each other. Then I said prayers, mentioning our burdens, but not mentioning Mutombo. Then everyone was shown a place to sleep.

Ngalula and I went to bed. Now we were alone. I could speak to her about these things without fear.

"When did Mbuyi and the children arrive?" I asked.

"They arrived yesterday when the sun was high. They came in a truck. It was coming with soldiers from the fighting. It was taking wounded soldiers to the hospital."

"Does she know truly that Mutombo is dead? Or were they separated in the fighting?"

"I did not want to ask her many questions. She said the fighting was bad. She said the rebels killed many people. She said they killed Mutombo. While she and the children hid in the jungle, her tenth child died of hunger. It was thirteen moons old. She has no hope of seeing Mutombo again upon earth."

As I lay in the darkness, pictures of many different kinds passed through my mind.

"Ngalula, I can't accept that Mutombo is dead. If they really killed him, do you know what burden has caught me?"

"Yes. You are the caretaker of the things of your deceased elder brother. It would mean that you have become the father of nine children."

After much time had passed, I heard Ngalula making the sounds of sleep. But for me sleep had fled from this night. My heart kept troubling me with questions. My mind gave me pictures of many things, hooked one to the other. When the first rooster crowed, none of my questions had been answered. I arose and prayed until sufficient light came for me to read.

When the sun arose, the children began awaking. I helped Mbuyi bathe them while Ngalula worked in the kitchen. When the sun was up well, she brought us food. The children ate well. I begged Mbuyi to eat. She shook her head. I did not have hunger. We could not continue thus forever. I was as an egg forgotten for many days, about to burst its shell. I could not pass more hours without knowing.

"Mbuyi, could I ask questions about what happened? Would it make your burden heavier?"

"No," she replied. "Talking about it may cause me to weep, but it may lighten my sorrow."

"Do you know truly that Mutombo died? Perhaps the fighting drove him into the jungle to hide."

"No. They killed him before my eyes. He died in my arms."

Had her mind cracked? Could she say this, it not being true? Then Mutombo must truly be dead. While we talked now, he was already with Jesus. The truth of this matter fell inside me and hit the bottom of my stomach. My whole body was weak.

"Why did they kill him?"

"For nothing. He died like Jesus. He had no bad thoughts in his heart. Bad people killed him for nothing."

She paused and sighed to restrain her grief. Then she spoke again. "When the rebels arrived, they did not first go into the town. They first came to the mission post. It is outside of town, as you know. They were Amputu tribesmen. They wanted to show everyone in town that they were powerful. They wanted to do something very bad to a person everybody knew; then no one would have courage to lift a finger against them.

"They had chosen Mutombo to be this person. They hunted for a way to accuse him. They said we who sat on the mission post were hiding things which helped the government soldiers fight against them. They wanted to see what we had inside our houses. One of our missionaries had gone on vacation; he had locked his house. Rebels did not believe that we did not have the key to that house. They broke down the door and entered it. They hunted in the white man's things for a long time. Finally they found an empty metal box which long ago had had some cartridges in it. They said, 'This shows plainly that you have been helping our enemies. For this crime, we must kill either the white man or his Congolese helper.' They sent word to their commander, asking him who should die.

240

"While they waited for a reply from their commander, Mutombo called me and the children. We sat together on the steps in front of the missionary's house. He looked at me eye to eye and said, 'I see that today God has seen fit for my journey on earth to end. When this happens, don't accuse God. Remember all the years of joy we have had living together. Remember the children He has given us. Above everything, bring up the children in the path of the book of God.' "

Mbuyi stopped talking. She wiped her cheeks with her skirt.

"Then they came with the answer. Mutombo was to die. They shot him in the back with a stuttering gun. They shot him, me and the children watching with our eyes. When he fell to the ground, I ran to him. I sat on the ground and picked him up by his shoulders. He tried to lift himself, he breathed one time, his chest fell, he died."

Thus it was true that Mutombo had left earth forever. The burden of his children now became mine. But other questions remained.

"When the rebels ruled over the town, did they cause much suffering?"

"First they killed the government leaders. They wanted to kill the missionary; instead they beat him and made him and his wife stay inside their house. From time to time they would kill someone who disrespected them, but some days passed when no one was killed. It was thus for most of the days they ruled over us. Then word came that the rebels had been defeated on the road to Malandi. The rebel leaders made the townspeople stay inside their houses. Then we heard big guns talking far away. We knew the army was coming. The rebels saw that they could not keep the town. If they could not keep it, they did not want to leave it without tormenting those they had hoped to rule over. Before they fled, they tied the doors of people's houses shut and set the grass roofs on fire. Thus many of the townspeople burned up in their houses."

"How did you escape?"

"The mission post is on a hill. When we heard the big guns talking and saw the roofs of houses burning, I took the children and fled. We did not have time to take many things. Badibanga, the oldest boy, has a quiet heart like his father's. He helped me gather blankets, clothing and a few cooking dishes. Odia, our baby, did not have a strong body. I knew that by living in the jungle she might catch sickness and die. But what I had seen with my eyes made me very afraid. I feared these wicked ones, these men with black hearts. If I stayed, they would kill all of us. Thus we fled into the jungle."

"Did others flee with you, or were you alone?"

"Others fled also, but each group hunted its own path. Thus in the jungle we were alone."

"Did Odia suffer much in dying?"

"All of us suffered. Hunger tormented us. At first we were strangers in the jungle. Slowly we learned to know it. When it became light each day, the children would go hunt for food. I told them to never go far; I greatly feared a rebel would find them. One who has been bitten by a snake fears even the head of a lizard.

"They promised each other that when one of them found something to eat, he would bring it to me; thus we could divide it. They brought me berries, roots, grasshoppers, flying ants. Each day, when the sun had lowered and trees no longer had shadows, we divided among us what we had. But we would never start a fire. We feared rebels would see it and come looking for us. Thus we ate everything as it was, without cooking it.

"We did not have enough blankets. Thus I sat up at night

holding Odia in my arms. She got warmth from my body, but she did not rest well. Many times she cried weakly. I feared the rebels might hear her, but I could not quiet her. I came to understand that she was crying from hunger. Because I ate so little, my breasts had no milk. If I failed to eat more food, Odia would die. It would be good for me to take a larger portion of the food for myself so that Odia could have milk and live. But would the children accept for me to take a larger portion of what they found? If they ate less, would weakness and sickness not catch them too?

"Badibanga made a small trap. One day he caught a rat. When the children returned at the end of that day and saw the rat, they leaped and danced with happiness. 'Let us start a fire, Mother,' they said. 'Let us cook the rat. Tonight we will eat well.'

"I could not ruin their happiness. They gathered firewood and started a little fire. I prayed that no one would see it. When it came time to divide the rat among us, I decided to save for myself a larger portion. I began dividing the rat into ten portions. Each portion was shamefully small. The children's eyes were fastened on my hands as I divided it. With them watching me thus, could I save for myself a larger portion? I fought inside myself. Then I remembered a custom of our forefathers and I felt at peace.

"Do you remember how our tribesmen did long ago when an enemy tribe was fighting them and threatened to triumph over them? They would choose a young girl and offer her as a living sacrifice. They would pack wet clay around her living body, building a pillar around her, until she was covered. This living fetish gave our tribesmen power to overcome their enemies. Thus one person sacrificed would save the lives of many. I could not save myself a larger portion of the rat. We would divide it equally. Perhaps I would have to offer Odia as a sacrifice. We thanked Mvidi

Mukulu for our food. We ate. That night the children slept well. When two more nights passed, Odia died and we buried her. The children grieved. I too was sad. But in my heart, I saw that God had taken the offering. Thus I hoped that those of us who remained would be saved."

"How did you come out of the forest and arrive here?"

"Another evening we had started a fire. We were cooking things we had found. Suddenly there was a noise behind me and the children looked at one place above me, with fear and surprise. I turned, and saw a young rebel soldier with a gun. He was standing behind me. I was terribly afraid, but there was no way of fleeing. I asked him to sit with us at the fire.

"He asked about us. I told him of our troubles. I told him how Mutombo had died. I told him how Odia had died. I told him we were simple people of God. We had no affair in politics. We had the blood of no one on our hands. I begged him not to deliver us into the hands of those who might cause us more suffering. As I talked, I watched his face closely. When I began, his eyes showed me that his heart was as a stone. But after begging him to have love for us, I saw that his heart appeared to soften. He said he would not trouble us tonight. The children should sleep, he said, then we could talk about these things as adults.

"I put out the fire, the soldier watching me closely. I wrapped the children in their blankets. Then I sat among them and prayed aloud. I told Mvidi Mukulu how the birds and animals had places to sleep and the things they needed to eat because they trusted Him. I told Him that we were much more precious than they, but we trusted Him for all things just as they did. Thus He would care for us and give us what we needed to be happy, as all His creatures of the jungle were. I also asked our Father in the sky to take care of the rebel soldier and to guide him into paths of truth and happiness. Then I asked Him to guard us from all evil during the darkness of night.

"The soldier and I talked about many things. I felt inside of me that he accepted the things I had told him to be true. He did not accuse me of lying. When much time had passed, he asked what I would pay him if he would lead me to those who could help me. I told him I had no money. He asked me if I could not pay with some of the things I had with me. I asked him what he wanted. He said he would accept two blankets. I told him that I could not lose the blankets; the children would suffer at night without them. He said if I accepted his word, before another night came I would be in the hands of those who could give me all I needed. Again fighting rose within me. If he was lying, our blankets would be lost and our suffering would pass us up in greatness. If he was telling the truth, we would be saved. Something tried to tell me that he was not lying. I agreed to give him the blankets. He said we would begin our journey when the darkness of night broke.

"When the light of morning came, he took us through jungle we had never seen before. We walked until the sun began to warm the earth; then we came onto a motorcar path.

" 'I am leaving you now,' he said. 'If you wait here, those who can help you will find you.'

"But why are you leaving us here?" I asked. "The road is strange. We are lost people. Where will we go if no one comes?

" 'If you leave here, trouble may catch you. If you wait here, helpers will come. They pass this way every day. Stay well.'

"He put our two blankets under his arm and disappeared into the jungle. My heart troubled me. Perhaps he had deceived us for the purpose of getting our blankets. Then what suffering would catch us when night came! But if he wanted our blankets, he did not have to deceive us to get them. He had a gun. He could have taken our blankets by force. He could have taken all our things. He could have killed us in the jungle, and no person would ever have known what had happened. But he did not. His words must be true. We sat to wait.

"When the sun was high and hot, we heard the noise of a machine. I stood to look. I saw a big truck full of government soldiers. The small children pulled on my skirt, trying to hide. The larger ones stood with me and waved for the soldiers to stop. Their guns were pointed at us. They stopped. I told them our troubles. I begged them to help us. They lowered their guns. They told us to get into the truck. They took us to their camp. They put us in a truck with some wounded soldiers. That truck brought us here to your village."

I had never before known the heart of Mbuyi well. Now I saw her to be a strong, brave woman. She had spoken. Her burden of suffering had lightened. All my questions were answered.

✿　✿　✿

The child being carried knows nothing; only its father knows the end of the journey.

23

I was not happy for the death of Mutombo. But as I sat thinking about it my eyes slowly opened and I began to understand the wisdom of God. Coming to understand His wisdom, I was comforted.

There are not many times when a man receives nine children in one day. This is why God did not accept to give Ngalula and me children in our bodies. He knew that the day was coming when we would receive the burden of an entire family. If we had had children of our own, now how could we carry this burden well? Thus our hunger for children was finished.

There were five girls and four boys; the oldest boy was with the age of sixteen years, the youngest was a boy with the age of two years. The older ones were with sufficient strength to help us in our fields. We could make large fields now. Harvest from these fields would bring us the wealth we needed. The two older girls would soon enter marriages. This also would bring me wealth. This was the wisdom Mvidi Mukulu had arranged long ago, which when sufficient days had passed, would lighten my burdens. Soon my uncles, Tshibuabua and Kabambi, already aged, would receive back the rest of the money I owed them. On top of this they would receive a gift for their kindness of having helped me. Thus the burdens which had troubled me all these years were ended. We had children, and my debts were finished.

One evening I was sitting outside of my house thinking of these things. The sun had already entered its place of sleeping. The wind-voices of the spirits had begun talking in the treetops. It was cool. Ngalula brought some coals and firewood from the kitchen. She started a fire at my feet. When the children saw it, they came running and sat down before me. For a time they sat quietly, warming themselves, watching the fire. Then one of them looked at me and said, "Uncle, could you tell us a story like Father used to do?"

I had not yet become accustomed to being a father. I knew God had revealed to me some measure of His wisdom, but I felt within me now that the wisdom He had kept for Himself was much and what He had given me was little. I needed wisdom now. I needed it that I might be able to tell the children a story. They had not complained, but I knew that inside them, their hearts were troubled. The length of their journey on earth had been a few years, but what their eyes had seen, what their ears had heard, what their bodies had felt, would distress the heart of an old man. I wanted my story to help them understand the hard affairs which had caught them and which had caught all of us during these last years. In understanding these things better, their hearts might be quieted. Thus I began my story.

One day a crocodile was lying on the sand beside the river. The sun was bright. The sand warmed his stomach. He was sleeping happily.

All at once he was awakened by the voices of chattering animals. He lifted up his long nose to see who was troubling his rest. The large branch of a tree stuck out toward him and in it three monkeys were eating berries with much joy.

"What?" the crocodile cried. "Just three little no-good animals. What nerve you have to ruin my sleep! What are you doing here? Don't you know I'm chief of the river? Aren't you afraid of me? Go hunt your little berries another place."

"Why do you despise little animals hunting berries?" one of the monkeys asked. "Don't judge things that you don't understand. You may be chief of the river, but you aren't chief of the trees. Sometimes chiefs with little bodies rule over chiefs with big bodies. Haven't you learned this?"

"What are you saying?" replied the crocodile. "Do you mean that you, a useless, weak thing, could rule over me? How great the brazenness of a monkey to so offend me!"

"How do you know I'm a weak, useless thing when you have never tested my strength? A wise warrior does not boast until after the battle. Who knows? Perhaps my strength could pull you right out of your water. Then who would be chief of the river?"

"A monkey drag a crocodile? You're teasing me with useless chatter. How the animals of the forest would laugh at us! How they would make fun of me! You're wasting my time for nothing. Run along and stop bothering me. I want to sleep."

"It is well," said the monkey. "We will leave you. But we will tell everyone that now we are chiefs of the river."

"What? You will NOT tell people you are chiefs of the river. Do you hear? I am chief of the river. No one here is stronger than I am."

"What forbids us to say that we are chiefs of the river? We play along the river all the time. We are chiefs of the river until someone shows us that he is stronger than we are. To talk is easy; to do is hard. There are many chiefs who talk, but they are worthless. It is the chief who shows his strength who is honored."

"So you want me to show my strength? If it is thus, come back with a strong pulling vine this time tomorrow. I'll take vengeance on you. I'll pull you into the middle of the river and drown you. Then all your monkey friends will fear me;

they will eat their berries at other places, and I will sleep well."

So the monkey who was going to test the strength of the crocodile told his two friends to make a long rope by tying vines together. Then he ran through the trees until he found a big elephant.

"Friend elephant, you must help me with a big affair tomorrow," the monkey said.

"I help those who are able to help me back," said the elephant.

"There are things I can do to help you back," said the monkey.

"What can a little animal like you do to help me?"

"Your eyes are weak. Because of this, you must work hard to find things to eat. You lose much time breaking paths through the jungle to where there is no food. I have strong eyes. I run here and there easily in the tops of the trees. I can lead you to where there are trees about to break because of their burden of fruit. I can lead you to bushes covered with soft sugar leaves."

"Your help would be welcome," the elephant said. "What do you want me to do?"

"The crocodile offended us today. He boasted of his strength. He acted as if he were chief of all the beasts of the jungle. I asked him to prove his strength by pulling me. He told me to come tomorrow with a pulling vine. Let us go make him ashamed. With your help, friend elephant, I will pull him out of the river to the top of the hill!"

"The growling of that crocodile has bothered me many times," said the elephant. "His boasts aggravate me. I will help you. After tomorrow, the crocodile will stay under the water, hiding in shame."

News spread through the jungle that the monkey and crocodile were going to test each other's strength. When the time arrived, many different kinds of animals had gathered to watch. The monkey's two helpers had done as he had told them. They took one end of the pulling vine out of the forest and placed it in the water for the crocodile to hold it. In the forest, where no one could see, they untied the vine. The end of the piece that went to the river was tied to the rear leg of the elephant; the end of the other piece, the elephant held in his trunk. Then they stretched out the second piece of vine so that it came out of the jungle into an open place where everybody could see it. The monkey picked up the end of the vine in his tail and waited. He was ready to pull.

The animals saw that the crocodile was holding one end and the monkey was holding the other. They cried out at one time. The monkey pulled with all his strength. The crocodile fought with his feet. He dug with his claws into the sand. He tried to hold onto rocks. But he was not able to stay in the river. His body was pulled out of the water. It was pulled across the sand. It was pulled into the forest. Then the crocodile let go of the vine and ran back into the river, and with much shame, disappeared into the water.

All the animals cried out in happiness for the monkey. "What a surprising affair!" they said to each other. "If we had not seen it with our eyes, we would not accept it. This finishes everybody's doubts. The monkey is master of the crocodile. The monkey is chief of the river."

I sat quietly, that they might think about this story. Then I spoke.

"My children, let me explain this fable for you. We, the people of this country, were sitting quietly in the sun. We were happy. Then a word arrived. It began troubling us. It did not accept for us to sit quietly. It was 'dipanda.'

251

"We thought it was a word with little strength. To conquer this word would be an easy affair. Then we would be chiefs of ourselves. There would no longer be a person saying, 'Bow down to me.'

"But the word dipanda tricked us. There was power inside of it that we did not know about. People wanted to throw away all the chiefs that were over them. They did not understand that every man must worship a chief. People who have learned how to walk with Jesus worship God as their chief. They sit quietly together. They are at peace. People who have not accepted the chieftainship of Mvidi Mukulu think they are big chiefs of themselves. But really they are slaves to other chiefs—chiefs of selfishness, greed, lust, enmity. Because these chiefs rule them, they cannot sit at peace with others. They fight each other. Because of their fighting, people who have no sympathy with them are caused to suffer with them.

"Thus during these years our earth has been troubled. Many people have suffered. Many people have died. This is because we have not yet conquered the word dipanda. The word has much power. This power will build our country into a place of happiness when we, the people of this country, accept that God is our great Chief. When people truly give Him homage, they will sit quietly together. When we do this, we will have shown everybody that we are chiefs of the river. The word dipanda will have become our servant."

By this time the moon had risen. The older children sat quietly thinking, looking into the fire. The smaller children looked at me with faces of happiness. Then as the custom of little children is, they arose and went to play in the great open space where the moon whitened the earth between our huts.

O Earth beneath us,
You have heard all of man's footsteps;
You guard them within you, and wonder.

Our forefathers went into slavery;
You saw them struggling to stand.
You saw them returning from slavery
Marching tall, as men among men.

They came marching and singing,
Hoping to harvest earth's riches.
But no one had taught them of freedom,
And so darkness of battle enclosed us.

Men killed those who walked with us.
Blood flowed down as a river.
Men destroyed men, hunting freedom,
And found that again, they were slaves.

Oh great elder Spirit in the sky,
Too bright for the sun to look at,
You sit at the start of our journey
And see all things, clear to its end.

Teach us the freedom of worship
That redeems the body from slavery,
That honors Thee as a Father
Who loves us and watches our footsteps.

Make us as the bird in the jungle
On a high branch, singing bravely,
Singing to worship its Master
Because its spirit is free.

Give us faith that leans strongly,
Unchanging and pure, like the moonlight,
To conquer all troubles that catch us,
To cause us to rise again, singing.

Faith with more power than dawa,
With magic that cannot be broken,
Which will make us strong warriors in battle,
Warriors who make men truly free.